THE
RED KITE

THE
RED KITE

by
Ian Carter

ARLEQUIN PRESS

ISBN 1 900159 61 9

First published 2001

Arlequin Press, 26 Broomfield Road, Chelmsford, Essex CM1 1SW

Text: © Ian Carter
Map: © Arlequin Press
Illustrations: © Dan Powell

A catalogue record for this book is available.

Dedication

To the gamekeepers, farmers and landowners in the Red Kite release areas in Britain, without whose help the reintroduction programme would not have been possible.

Adult Red Kite and small chicks at the nest *(Carlos Sanchez Alonso)*

ACKNOWLEDGEMENTS

My involvement with the Red Kite began, in 1995, with the start of the central England reintroduction project and I would firstly like to thank those individuals who made this work possible. Hose Lara Zabia and Maria Teressa Tarazona provided invaluable help in arranging for nestlings to be collected from central Spain, and permission to take birds was granted by the Junta de Castilla y León (Dirección General del Medio Natural). Many individuals were involved in collecting nestlings from Spain and I would like, in particular, to thank Ian Evans, Phil Grice, Rod Hall, Karl Ivens, Charlie Rugeroni, Peter Stevens, Robert Thomas and Jonathan Wray. In addition, the Southern England Kite Group (Mick McQuaid, Nigel Snell and Peter Stevens) helped with the translocation of Kites within England, and Tony Cross and Nick Fox provided rescued young from central Wales.

I have shared the task of monitoring released birds and studying the subsequently re-established population with John Cornell, Derek Holman, Karl Ivens (Forest Enterprise), Momo Medina and Deborah Ottway. Robert Thomas has been a frequent companion in the field and has endured many bone-chilling winter evenings at the main communal roost in order to help gather information on wing-tagged birds.

I have learnt a great deal over the past five years through conversations with others involved in Red Kite conservation in Britain, some with many, many years of experience of the bird: Colin Crooke, Tony Cross, Alistair Crowle, Peter Davis, Will Dixon, Kevin Duffy, Brian Etheridge, Robert Kenward, Mick McQuaid, Duncan Orr-Ewing, Lorcan O'Toole, David Parkin, Doug Simpson, Nigel Snell, Peter Stevens and Peter Walters Davies have all helped to increase my understanding of the Red Kite. Roger Clarke's expertise was invaluable during studies of diet and, as author of the first volume in this series, it was he who first suggested that the Kite would make an ideal subject for a book of this nature.

Andy Brown and Phil Grice at English Nature provided several useful historical references, unearthed during work on their forthcoming book, *Birds in England*. Chris Monk helped to set up a database of records from studies of radio-tagged and wing-tagged birds in central England, from which much information on survival rates, dispersal, home range and habitat-use has been derived. He also helped to collate information on the Kite's breeding status in Europe. David Conlin and Selena Carter translated several recent German publications into English, making accessible some very useful accounts of the species in its central European stronghold.

Information on the main mortality factors currently affecting Kites in England has been built up as a result of post-mortems carried out by Andrew Cunningham, Tracey Howard, James Kirkwood, Tony Sainsbury and Sue Thornton at the Zoological Society of London, Institute of Zoology. Pesticide residues in Kite tissues were determined by analysis at the Central Science Laboratory and the Centre for Ecology and Hydrology, and Mark Fletcher (CSL), Richard Shore (CEH), Alastair Burn (English Nature) and Peter Karner (Farming and Rural Conservation Agency) have provided much guidance on this subject.

The following staff at RSPB (in addition to some of the individuals named above) have been directly involved with work on the Red Kite in England and are thanked for their help: Katherine Davies, Graham Elliot, Richard Gregory, Steve Holliday, Julian Hughes, Duncan McNiven, Peter Newbery, Guy Shorrock and Simon Wotton.

Andy Brown, Brian and Margaret Carter, Tony Cross, Brian Etheridge, Mike Gaydon, Phil Grice, Peter Newbery, Doug Simpson and Javier Viñuela made many invaluable comments on the text that greatly improved the final result.

CONTENTS

List of Tables

List of Figures

List of Plates

INTRODUCTION

The Red Kite is one of only a handful of birds that manages to thrill and delight almost everyone that is lucky enough to see it at close quarters. It has all the attributes required for attracting attention and admiration, including a spectacular plumage, a wonderfully graceful and effortless flight, and the habit of drifting slowly, low over the countryside, where it can be appreciated to full effect. It is, quite simply, one of the world's most impressive birds of prey.

During the relatively short period in which I have been involved with the Red Kite (for simplicity often referred to as the 'Kite'), I have been repeatedly amazed by the bird's appeal, even to people who have only a casual interest in wildlife. In the reintroduction areas in England and Scotland the Kite has become a frequent topic of conversation, and anything up to 200 people have packed into tiny village halls in order to learn more about this new addition to their local countryside. Farmers, gamekeepers and others who spend long hours working outdoors are often particularly enthusiastic as they have more opportunity than most to become familiar with the bird.

The Kite is a highly adaptable, generalist species, able to thrive in a wide range of different landscapes provided that the basic requirements of woodland for nesting and roosting, and open areas for foraging, are met. The species has one of the most varied diets of any European bird of prey and will scavenge on almost anything, from the smallest of birds and mammals to the largest of our domestic animals, as well as taking live prey in the form of small mammals, birds and invertebrates. In times gone by, even urban areas provided a home for the Kite, and the species was given special protection in Britain for its valuable role in helping to keep the streets clean.

Despite the Kite's lack of specialist habitat requirements, it has a rather patchy distribution across Europe, and is absent from some areas where the landscape appears to be perfectly suitable. This is mainly a reflection of the bird's extreme vulnerability to human persecution. It is relatively fearless of man and so is a regular victim of shooting and, as a scavenger, it often falls victim to illegal poison baits placed out in the open countryside. In areas where levels of persecution are low, the Kite usually thrives and populations have increased dramatically in some countries during the last ten years or so. But where persecution is still common practice, the Kite is either absent completely or its numbers are in worrying decline.

The story of the Red Kite in Britain emphasises the degree to which the bird's fortunes have changed at the hands of man. From being one of our most widespread and familiar birds of prey a few hundred years ago, the Kite came to within a hair's breadth of extinction by the end of the 19th century, as, along with other birds of prey, it was seen as a threat to gamebirds and livestock. A few pairs found a last refuge in the remote uplands of central Wales, where persecution was less intense, but where the damp, cool climate and unproductive landscape made recovery a painfully slow process. Thankfully, we live in times when attitudes towards birds of prey in Britain, at least amongst a majority of people, have changed for the better. The lack of fear of man that once hastened the Kite's decline is now an asset, allowing it to exploit food sources close to human settlements and providing people with spectacular views as its drifts slowly overhead. In parts of Britain the Kite has, once again, become a regular visitor to rural villages and the edges of small towns and it will even come down to food put out for it in village gardens. A photograph of one bird in the process of snatching up the leftovers of someone's Sunday lunch appeared recently in the national press, and in the accompanying interview, the householder expressed his delight at being able to watch such a magnificent bird from the comfort of his own living room.

One of the most fascinating aspects of the Kite is its highly social behaviour in winter. Groups of anything up to several hundred birds gather together at traditional roosts in the late afternoon, often indulging in spectacular communal display-flights above the roost wood, before settling in the trees for the night. At times, the birds seem to be simply enjoying themselves and it is a highly uplifting experience to watch a pre-roost gathering of Kites wheeling around in tight formation, with some breaking away from the main group to indulge in rapid, zig-zagging chases. Despite the apparent frivolity of this activity, there are good biological reasons for communal roosting, as well as the pre-roost display-flights, and these are explored in the chapter on 'social behaviour and play'.

A huge amount of time and resources have been put into efforts to conserve the Red Kite in Britain, both in central Wales, where the once tiny population has now made a substantial recovery, and in England and Scotland where the bird has been reintroduced. The fact that Government-funded bodies, conservation charities and, in some cases, private companies, have been willing to fund this work demonstrates the importance placed on restoring native species that have been lost as a result of our own thoughtless actions in the past. Similar projects have been undertaken with many other birds of prey across Europe and North America, further highlighting both the vulnerability of this group of birds, sitting at the top of the food chain, and the high value placed on their presence in the countryside.

Perhaps the most extreme example of a bird restoration project is the ongoing effort in the western United States to save the California Condor from extinction. A conservation programme has now been running for over 20 years, involving research into the reasons for decline, captive-rearing, and reintroductions at several different sites. A very rough estimate of costs suggests an annual figure in excess of one million dollars and there is still a long way to go before the work can be regarded as successful in ensuring the survival of the species.

Although the cost of the Kite reintroduction programme falls well short of the amount spent on the California Condor, it nevertheless attracts criticism from some who think that too much money is spent on a minority of high profile species, at the expense of other, more pressing, conservation priorities. It is therefore important to emphasise that well-planned reintroduction projects are not simply about restoring a single species. They can be used to try to promote more wildlife-friendly forms of landscape management and to tackle problems that affect a whole range of different species. The Red Kite reintroduction pro-gramme has helped to show that illegal poison baits still threaten birds of prey in Britain and has highlighted problems with accidental secondary poisoning when highly toxic anticoagulant poisons are used to control rodents. The Kite has proved to be a very useful 'flagship' species in trying to tackle these problems and, as well as helping the Kite to increase and spread, this will undoubtedly benefit other species, such as the Buzzard and Barn Owl, that are also affected by the same problems.

Chapter 1

DESCRIPTION AND TAXONOMY

Most people who have had the opportunity to watch Red Kites at close quarters will agree that, quite simply, this is one of our most beautiful and spectacular birds of prey. The plumage is a rich mixture of rufous, brown and black, with contrasting large white 'windows' on the underwings, and a long, deeply forked, reddish-brown tail. It is in flight that the Kite's full beauty is revealed and its habit of floating slowly, low over open country, together with a relative lack of fear of humans, means that the plumage is often shown off to full effect. With many birds of prey the most frequent views are of a small dot circling high in the sky or a shape, barely registered, as it flashes past at high speed. The Kite often allows a more prolonged and considered appraisal, and, with its impressive five-foot wingspan and varied colours, rarely disappoints the observer.

Even at a considerable distance the Kite's distinctive cruciform shape, with long, angled wings and long tail, together with its buoyant, effortless flight make it an easy bird to recognise, particularly in areas where the similar Black Kite does not occur. When perched, much of the contrast between different coloured areas of plumage is lost and the bird appears a rather uniform reddish-brown colour, with only the pale head, and yellow eye and bill, standing out.

Plumage

Full descriptions of plumage can be found in many excellent field guides and handbooks (e.g. Svensson *et al* 1999; Forsman 1999; Jonsson 1992) and are therefore not repeated in detail here. A fair appreciation of the bird may be gained from the photographs (see plates 1, 2 & 4) but they do not do full justice to a bird that derives so much of its appeal from the gracefulness and agility of its flight. As with all birds, there is no substitute for direct observation in the field.

The only species with which the Red Kite is likely to be confused is its close relative the Black Kite. This species is a rare summer visitor to Britain but is very common in summer in much of the Red Kite's Continental range. Given good views, the Red Kite's longer, more deeply forked, reddish tail and reddish-brown plumage on the body and wing coverts are distinctive. The Black Kite (see plate 3) has a much darker plumage with comparatively shorter wings and tail. With practice, the distinctive colours and shapes of the two species can be picked out, even at considerable distance. The main risk of confusion is in late summer when recently fledged young are on the wing. These juvenile birds are more compact than the adults, with slightly shorter wings and a shorter, less deeply forked, tail. Close scrutiny of young Red Kites is required to reveal the pale reddish upper-tail and reddish tinge to the body and wing coverts that are not present on Black Kites of any age.

Juvenile Red Kites remain separable from adults until their first moult is complete in the following autumn. As well as their paler, more washed out appearance and the differences in shape already described, there are a number of other features worth looking for when trying to age a Kite. In late summer and early autumn, when juveniles are in fresh plumage, older birds will be moulting and many will have a rather tatty appearance with missing feathers and noticeable gaps in the wings or tail. The plumage of juveniles, by contrast, is usually immaculate with not a feather out of place, giving them a pristine appearance. In flight, the pale fringes to the wing coverts form a pale line across both the underwing and upperwing of juveniles, and this can be visible at a considerable distance in good light. On a perched bird the pale line formed by the upperwing covert fringes is visible on the folded wing, and the darker eye and paler markings on the underbody should also be apparent at close range (see plate 4).

In late summer, given close views, three age classes are readily separable – recently fledged young (as described above), young fledged in the previous year and adult birds at least two years old. Young from the previous year and adults will be in moult at this time of year but the younger birds still show signs of their immaturity until the moult nears completion in the autumn. The pale tips on the older, unmoulted wing-coverts remain (although they may be reduced as a result of wear), the underbody is still rather pale in comparison to the richer and more heavily streaked appearance of the adults, and the older, unmoulted, tail feathers are clearly paler than those that have already been replaced.

The plumage of Kites is generally very consistent and there is certainly not the wide degree of variation between individuals that is shown by the Common Buzzard for example. It is usually only possible to recognise an individual Kite if a wing or tail feather is damaged or missing, or, for a short time, by a distinctive pattern of gaps in the wings or tail during the annual moult. A very low proportion of birds, however, appear noticeably paler than normal and, in extreme cases, they may lack most of the dark pigmentation to the feathers, appearing almost pure white. Several of these white birds have occurred in Wales and have managed to survive for several years in some cases, although none have yet been found breeding (Cross & Davis 1998). In Germany, Hille (1995a) was able to recognise individual pale birds that returned to the same breeding site for up to four consecutive years.

Moult

Kites renew their flight and tail feathers in a single, protracted moult during the summer. Non-breeding birds, particularly juveniles, usually begin earlier than breeding adults and the distinctive gaps in the wings, as the first feathers are dropped, can be seen from late March onwards.

Breeding adults do not usually start to moult until the incubation phase of the breeding cycle in April or May and it is often the female that begins first. She spends almost all of her time sitting on the nest during the four weeks of incubation and the first 2-3 weeks after the eggs have hatched, and this provides an ideal opportunity to replace as many of the flight feathers as possible. During this period the female often has very noticeable gaps in the wings while the male has only small gaps or is still full-winged. This difference between the sexes is not entirely consistent as, in some cases, the male has gaps in the wings early in the season whilst the female remains full-winged well into incubation.

During the summer Kites are frequently seen with obvious gaps at the same point in each wing due to the loss of moulted feathers

Moulted feathers are often found close to breeding sites. This series from a nest site in central England includes two tail feathers (with a rufous wash), one of the long, mainly black, outer primaries, and a shorter and paler inner primary (Ian Carter)

Differences in moult pattern can be a very useful method of distinguishing between the two members of a breeding pair at a distance, particularly if marks such as colour rings or wing-tags can be used to confirm the identity of each individual when seen at close range.

Moult progresses from the inner primary (the first feather to be lost) towards the tip of the wing in a regular pattern, with the outermost primary last in the sequence. The pattern of moult of the secondaries is less predictable and some, particularly non-breeding, birds can have several gaps in the wings when moult is well advanced. The moult of the twelve tail feathers begins with the two central feathers and appears to progress, in sequence, from the centre to the edge of the tail. By September, the two outer tail feathers, falling short of the tip of the tail, may be the only sign that the moult is not yet complete. In migratory populations in central and northern Europe, moult is not usually completed by the time of the autumn migration and the last feathers are replaced in the winter quarters (Forsman 1999).

It is probable that Kites are able to suspend moult during the breeding season, as is known to occur in other raptor species. Individually marked birds with obvious gaps in the wings early in the breeding season are sometimes full-winged only a few weeks later, well before the time when moult could have been completed. It may be advantageous to suspend, or slow the rate of moult at a stage in the breeding cycle when more active flight is required, such as during the chick rearing period, particularly if food is in short supply. Missing feathers reduce foraging efficiency and could therefore reduce the amount of food that the adults are able to bring to the nestlings. Moult appears to proceed more rapidly towards the end of the breeding season when the duties of rearing young are at an end and, as a result, birds tend to become less active, perching up in trees for long periods. At this time of year it is not unusual to drive through an area with a high density of Kites and yet see hardly a single adult bird in the air.

As with many large birds of prey, not all the flight feathers are always replaced during the annual moult. Kites in their second winter, after the completion of their first full moult, sometimes retain several juvenile secondaries and one or more of the outermost juvenile primaries. These feathers appear faded and are browner than the new feathers although this is extremely difficult to detect on a free-flying bird.

The body feathers and wing coverts are also replaced during the summer moult, except for a proportion of juveniles that replace some of these feathers during their first winter. Some individuals begin as early as September/October of their first year while others are still in full juvenile plumage in April of their second year (Forsman 1999).

This bird, found dead in its second winter, has retained five of its juvenile secondaries. These are visible as groups of two and three feathers that are faded brown, with worn tips, and slightly shorter than the adjacent adult feathers *(Ian Carter)*

Voice

For much of the year the Kite is mainly silent and calling is only occasionally heard during squabbles over food, or at communal pre-roost gatherings. In the breeding season the Kite becomes rather more vociferous, particularly close to the nest site. Members of a pair call to each other as part of the courtship ritual and calling is frequently heard when there is disturbance near to an active nest.

Bird calls and songs are extremely difficult to represent accurately in words and there is no substitute for learning sounds through hearing them in the field. The Kite's usual call is perhaps closest to that of a Buzzard but is higher in pitch and often with two or three shorter and rapidly repeated, slurred notes after the initial call. Svensson *et al* (1999) describe it as 'weee-ooh, ee oo, ee oo, ee oo' but there is much variation. In some situations the call is weak and wavering, almost hesitant, but, when a nest site is disturbed, calls are often loud and shrill, and repeated rapidly with real purpose. Somewhat unexpectedly, a brief snatch of song from a Blackbird, Song Thrush or Robin can, initially, be mistaken for the distant call of a Kite.

Differences between the sexes

In some birds of prey there is a noticeable size difference between the sexes with females tending to be larger and heavier than males. This is termed 'reversed size dimorphism' as, in most groups of bird, it is the male that is usually bigger than the female. The difference is at its most extreme in the Sparrowhawk where females can be up to 25% larger than males and twice the weight. In contrast, there is little difference in size and weight between male and female Kites, although females tend to be slightly larger and heavier on average.

According to Baker (1993) birds weighing less than 950g are likely to be males, whilst those above 1,230g are probably females. Most, however, fall between these weights and therefore cannot be reliably separated even in the hand. A sample of birds, about 12 weeks old, were weighed before release in central England. Twelve males (sexed from DNA in blood samples) ranged from 0.72-0.91kg with an average of 0.80kg, and 14 females ranged from 0.8-1.01kg, averaging 0.87kg. These figures are somewhat lower than those given by Baker, which is probably because the birds were youngsters, close to fledging age, and yet to make their first flight.

The following biometric measurements provided by Baker (1993) illustrate the degree of overlap in size between the sexes. The measurements are averages and ranges in millimetres, with the sample size in brackets:

	Male	Female
Wing length[1]	490, 448-532 (7)	503, 478-535 (20)
Tail length	327, 301-351 (5)	343, 314-376 (15)
Bill	27.4, 25.8-29.2 (7)	27.7, 25.6-29.9 (19)
Tarsus	53.2. 52-55 (4)	52.8, 51-54 (9)
Claw	22.2, 21.3-22.6 (3)	21.9, 20.6-23.8 (9)

[1] From carpal joint to wing tip

Although there is a degree of overlap in size it is occasionally possible to separate the sexes in the field at close range, when the male and female are seen together. When, for example, a pair are circling over a breeding site, the slight difference in bulk and resulting subtle differences in flight characteristics may be apparent.

Newton (1979) showed that size differences between the sexes are generally greatest in species that rely on the active hunting of live prey, and suggested that this allowed food resources to be partitioned. Female Sparrowhawks, for example, are able to capture considerably larger prey than males. In carrion feeding species, where the prey is not killed, such partitioning of food by size is not feasible, as, even if females were much larger than males, they would not gain access to new, larger, sources of food. The Red Kite is predominantly a scavenger but does, at times, also take live prey and so the small difference in size between the sexes fits well with Newton's ideas.

Taxonomy

The Red Kite's closest relative and the only other species within the genus *Milvus* is the Black Kite *Milvus migrans*. These two species share many similarities in appearance and behaviour, and even hybridise at times, producing offspring with features of both species. Hybrid pairs have been reported in Sweden and Germany, and Ortlieb's book *Der Rotmilan* (1989) includes photographs of a hybrid pair and an example of the resultant offspring. There are only two known races of Red Kite, the Cape Verde Kite, *Milvus milvus fasciicauda*, which is found only on this island group (and is on the verge of extinction), and the nominate *milvus* race which is found across the rest of the range. The Cape Verde Kite is smaller than the nominate race and has a plumage closer to that of the Black Kite, with which it apparently regularly hybridises. Birds from populations of the nominate *milvus* race in North Africa and the birds that formerly occurred on the Canary Islands are reported to be smaller than those in Europe (Glutz Von Blotzheim, Bauer & Bezzel 1971).

Recent genetic studies have shown that the closest relatives of the genus *Milvus* are buzzards in the genus *Buteo*, including the Common Buzzard, and Sea-eagles in the genus *Haliaeetus*, including the White-tailed Eagle. There are many other genera across the world that include species referred to as 'kites' but these are not closely related to the two *Milvus* species. In the case of the European Black-shouldered Kite and the American White-tailed, Mississippi and Snail Kites it is the shared feature of a forked tail that has no doubt resulted in the use of 'kite' in the common names.

Local names

The word 'kite' is derived from the Anglo-Saxon 'cyta' (which is supposedly onomatopoeic of the bird's call) and evolved to its present day form through the medieval word 'kyte'. An alternative name that is even older than 'kyte' is 'glede' or 'glead', derived from the old Saxon verb for gliding, but this has long since fallen into disuse. There is often confusion as to the exact meaning of the term 'kyte' in the seventeenth and eighteenth centuries as, in some areas, this word was used to denote any large bird of prey. To make matters even more complicated, 'kitt' or keat' was used for Buzzard in Devon, where the Kite was known exclusively as 'glede', and, in Ireland, 'kite' was used to denote the Hen Harrier. 'Puttock' is another name that was used for both Kite and Buzzard, predominantly in the Midlands and the eastern counties, although Shakespeare used it when referring specifically to the Kite. Other local names include 'scoul' (Cornwall), 'fork-tail' (Yorkshire), 'crouch-tail' (Essex) and 'Boda wennol' (roughly translating as swallow-hawk) in parts of Wales (Lovegrove 1990). In Scotland and Ireland there are many Gaelic names for the Kite including 'croman-cearc' or 'chicken-hawk', a name also used in parts of England.

Chapter 2

HISTORY IN BRITAIN

Over the centuries, the fluctuating fortunes of the Red Kite in Britain have, perhaps more than any other bird, been bound together with human activities and changing public attitudes. Until around 2,500 BC, when Neolithic man began to clear significant areas of the wildwood then covering most of Britain, birds requiring open country must have been rare or absent. The Kite, although dependent on woodland for nest and roost sites, spends the majority of its time, and finds almost all of its food, by foraging over open ground. As more and more land was cleared for agriculture, so the resulting patchwork landscape of small woods and fields became ever more suitable for Kites and, by Norman times, the species was one of our most widespread and familiar birds. From this high point, the Kite was drastically reduced in number at the hands of man, before changing attitudes, intensive conservation efforts and a certain amount of good fortune came just in time to prevent extinction.

Medieval Britain

In medieval times the Red Kite would have been a common sight wheeling low over the open countryside. It would also have been familiar to those living in some of our larger towns and cities, including London, where it made a living by scavenging amongst refuse on the filthy, unpaved streets. By the 15th century, visitors were commenting on the tameness and size of Kite flocks in London, and reporting how food was even snatched from the hands of children (Reid-Henry & Harrison 1988). In rural areas they were equally bold, as is evident from the following account by Colonel G. Montagu, writing in 1833:

> *A poor woman was washing some entrails in a stream of water, part of which extended a few yards out of the basket placed in the water: the hungry bird had long been hovering, viewing with anxious eye so delicious a bait, and took the opportunity of actually pouncing upon and carrying off a part, in spite of all the woman's efforts with hand and tongue, the latter of which might have alarmed a more powerful enemy.*

In parts of present-day Asia and Africa it is the Black Kite that fulfils the role of urban scavenger and this has led some to suggest that it was this species, and not the Red Kite, that occurred in our medieval towns. There is no evidence to support this claim and, to the contrary, descriptions of Kites from visitors to London familiar with both species, as well as bone remains from London and other areas, demonstrate conclusively that it was the Red Kite that thrived in medieval Britain. The Black Kite has probably never been other than a rare summer visitor.

Kites could only survive in urban areas because standards of sanitation in those days were poor, and animal waste simply thrown out onto the streets provided an abundant source of food. Scavenging by Kites, and also Ravens, helped to remove waste and so reduced the risk to human health from outbreaks of disease. In recognition of this street-cleaning role, both species were granted special protection in England and Wales under royal statute from the 15th century onwards, the first species to be protected for reasons other than hunting. The same protection did not extend to Scotland where James II, as early as 1457, encouraged the destruction of Kites and other species (Lovegrove 1990), a portent of what was to come throughout Britain.

DAN POWELL

The Kite in falconry

In Spain the Red Kite is known as Milano Real, or Royal Kite, and in France and Italy the names of Milan Royal and Nibbio Reale have the same meaning. These names do not refer to the majesty of the bird itself but rather to the pleasure it provided to royal hunting parties in the Middle Ages. Because of its accomplished all-round flying skills and habit of circling high in the air, royal falconers considered that the taking of a Red Kite was the very peak of achievement for a trained falcon. Only the larger falcons such as Lanners from North Africa and the Middle East, and possibly Gyr Falcons, could manage such a feat. Yarrell (1857) describes how an owl with a Fox's brush tied to its leg to impede its flight was trained to fly around in circles, acting as a decoy in order to attract a Kite to within range of the falconer's bird.

There appears to have been considerable rivalry between the English and French in this sport and James I was apparently prepared to spend as much as £1,000 in acquiring a cast of birds that could outdo the achievements of the French. Unfortunately, at a specially arranged demonstration that took place near Royston in Hertfordshire, the first Kite pursued rose to such a height that neither it or the trained falcon were ever seen again (Lovegrove 1990).

A decline in fortunes

The Kite's rapid downturn in fortunes occurred, for different reasons, in both urban areas and in the countryside. In towns and cities, where they had taken advantage of the filth and squalor of the medieval period, sanitation inevitably improved until there was simply nothing left for the Kite to eat. The last remaining breeding pair in London was recorded at Grey's Inn in 1777, although the odd bird was seen over the town well into the 1800s (Lovegrove 1990).

The situation was no better in rural areas where the Kite was blamed for taking free-range chickens and even livestock and, for this reason, had probably never been much appreciated by country dwellers. Along with other birds of prey and predatory mammals it was increasingly heavily persecuted as rural settlements grew and the human population increased. Unfortunately, the Kite's scavenging lifestyle and relative lack of fear of people made it a very easy bird to kill. Poisoning, in particular, was a highly effective, although totally indiscriminate, means of control and, as the Kite is very much a social species, a single bait would often have been enough to account for several birds. Traps, baited with animal carcasses or live prey were also used.

A variety of traps were in use for catching Kites and other species as early as the 16th century

The role of persecution

The decline of the Kite was so rapid during the 18th and early 19th centuries that some authors believed that persecution alone could not be responsible. Lilford (1883) suggested that a very severe winter might have caused the declines he noted in Northamptonshire and reported the views of a correspondent, while doubting them himself, that the draining of the fens might have been a factor in neighbouring Cambridgeshire. Harvie-Brown (1906) even suggested that the loss of many large trees to storms in the early 19th century could have reduced the availability of nesting sites. It is possible that such factors did affect populations at a local level but it is equally clear that it was widespread persecution that played the major role in the Kite's demise. Ticehurst (1934), writing about 'vermin' control in the parish of Tenterden, Kent describes just how common the Kite must once have been and gives a vivid impression of the scale of the subsequent destruction (see below). The reference to payment relates to the 1566 'Acte for the Preservacion of Grayne' which offered rewards for the heads of 'noyfull Fowles and Vermyn' in order to encourage their destruction:

*The Kite . . . was evidently a very numerous species and one or more
of these grand birds must have been a commonplace everyday sight as
they soared over the surrounding forest that formed such a suitable
home for them. Between 1654 and 1675 an average of not much more
than two a year were paid for, but during the next decade it becomes
evident how common the bird must have been, for during this time no
fewer than 380 were accounted for, with a maximum of 100 in a single
year. It sounds incredible in these days, and there is not much cause
for wonderment in the fact that, though no slackening in the general
campaign is manifest, the numbers of Kites killed in the next two years
dropped to thirteen and two respectively. If the same sort of thing was
going on in other Wealden parishes, no large raptorial bird could have
long withstood such a drain on its numbers and it is no surprise that
we no longer have any Kites with us.*

The birds and mammals listed in the 1566 act included such relatively
innocuous species as the Hedgehog, Bullfinch, woodpeckers, and, of course, the
unfortunate Kite. Churchwardens were responsible for making the payments and
often kept detailed parish records. The following are extracts for the parish of
Tenterden as reported by Ticehurst (1934), detailing payments in pounds,
shillings and pence:

1667-68

Paid to Thomas Jonas for 4 Raven's heads and 1 Hedgehogg's head . 0   0   4

To John Drew for 1 dozen of Crowe's heads and for 3 Kytes 0   0   8

To Wm. Baker for 4 Kytes, 1 Pulcat and 4 Raven's heads. 0   1   2

To John Morphett for 2 Kyte's heads, 4 Woodpeckers
and 8 Crowe's heads 0   0 10

1676-77
Ffrancis Peck for 3 dozen & halfe of Kyte's heads
and 1 Hedghogg's head. 0   1   1

Ticehurst suspected that the 1676-77 record, involving payment to one person
for no less than 42 Kite heads, probably related to nestlings rather than adults,
citing the lower than usual level of payment for each individual bird. He also
pointed out that this would represent the contents of approximately 15-20 nests
using a rough average of 2-3 young per nest. It is interesting that, although
records of bounty payments have been discovered for many areas of England

and Scotland, there are apparently none for Wales, where the Kite eventually found its last refuge.

Records from another part of the country show that persecution continued apace into the 19th century (Table 1) but, this time, with a new justification, the protection of gamebirds for shooting. The rearing and release of gamebirds on large sporting estates increased in popularity during the late 18th century and species seen as potential gamebird predators were simply not tolerated. Game-keepers were employed with predator control as one of their main responsibilities and birds of prey were targeted with an almost religious fervour that the already depleted and vulnerable Kite could not withstand for long.

Table 1: **Birds and mammals killed on the Burley Estate, Rutland, 1807-1816 (Squires & Jeeves 1994)**

Red Kites	183	Woodpeckers	103
Buzzards	285	Stoats	1,269
Hawks	340	Weasels	454
Owls	386	Polecats	206
Magpies	1,530	Pine Martens	9
Jays	428	Cats	554
Crows	1,603	Red squirrels	197
Jackdaws	1,798	Rats	17,108
Herons	24		

As well as using traps and poison baits, gamekeepers in the 19th century had a further option for controlling predators. The shotgun had evolved gradually since first developed for shooting game in the 16th century and was an increasingly effective weapon against birds of prey. The Kite's slow, languid foraging flights, often low over the ground, and its lack of fear of man, made it a particularly easy target for guns of ever improving accuracy.

As numbers continued to fall, the Kite became an increasing target for egg collectors and the taxidermy trade. The value of Kite eggs and skins increased as a direct result of their increasing rarity, offering ever greater financial incentives for collectors to pursue the bird, and driving it relentlessly towards extinction. It is perhaps no surprise that one of the last breeding records in England involved a female shot from its nest (near Bishop's Castle, Shropshire in 1863), while one of the last breeding pairs in Scotland (in Caithness, 1884) had its eggs taken and presented to the British Museum (Holloway 1996). Only in Wales did a handful of the 'old-race' of British Kites remain by the end of the 19th century.

The Red Kite in Wales

In the remote valleys of central Wales, away from the major sporting estates, the Red Kite clung on to a last refuge in Britain, hampered by the unproductive nature of the land, the unsuitable damp, cold summers and continued persecution, albeit at a lower level than in England and Scotland. It had been thought that the Kite population reached its lowest level in about 1905 and that only about five birds remained, but it is now known that numbers were always somewhat higher and the true low-point was not until some three decades later. Peter Davis has managed to piece together a reasonably complete picture of the Kite's changing fortunes in the first half of the 20th century using the diaries and unpublished accounts of those involved with Kite protection in Wales at the time, notably Professor J.F. Salter, Col. Morrey Salmon and E.G.B Meade-Waldo (Davis 1993). From these records it seems likely that at no time did the population fall much below ten territorial pairs and the total spring population, including immatures and unmated adults, was probably never lower than about 20 individuals.

An estimated population of 20 territorial pairs in the 1890s declined gradually to a low of about 10 pairs in the 1930s and early 1940s before starting the slow recovery, which continues to this day. Initially, this new information suggests that the Kite did not come quite as close to extinction as had previously been thought. However, recent genetic evidence, utilising sections of maternally inherited DNA, has helped to reveal a rather different picture. Blood samples taken from Welsh Kites in the late 1980s were analysed by researchers at Nottingham University (May, Wetton & Parkin 1993) and showed that, until relatively recently, all Kites in Wales were probably descended from just a single breeding female that passed through the genetic bottleneck when the population was at its lowest ebb. Although the total population was always at least 10 territorial pairs it seems that, at the low point, only a single breeding pair reared young that survived and subsequently went on to rear their own young. The population was therefore almost as close as it is possible to get to becoming extinct.

The genetic studies also showed that, at some point within the previous 20 years, an immigrant female joined the Welsh population. The new blood-line, detected in the DNA samples, corresponded closely to one found commonly in central European Kites and it is thought most likely that this was the origin of the immigrant.

Kite protection in Wales – the early years

Although Kites survived in central Wales as a result of lower levels of human persecution and interference, they were by no means totally free from such molestations, and, by the end of the 19th century, there was an urgent need for active protection of the remaining pairs. The story of Kite protection in Wales is a long and complex one, spanning more than 100 years, and probably represents the longest-running active bird protection scheme that has ever been carried out. Roger Lovegrove in his book *The Kite's Tale* (1990), upon which the account below is largely based, described the often convoluted and rarely uncontroversial events in some detail, making no attempt to hide the less savoury aspects of the period:

> *In a story as notable as this, it would be satisfying to be able to record the smooth and efficient progress of the successive schemes as the story evolved over the years. However, [one] of the remarkable aspects of Kite protection has been the extent to which it has been plagued over the years by bitter division, acrimonious clashes of personality, jealousies, intrigue and deception.*

Some of the earliest efforts to protect Kites took place in the mid-Wales county of Brecknock, and included the production of 'Instructions to Keepers', circulated via local landowners, and the payment of bounties for landowners willing to protect breeding pairs on their land. The system of bounty payments was to be a mainstay of protection for the greater part of the 20th century, and a constant reminder of just how much attitudes had changed since the days when financial rewards were offered for the destruction of Kites. Despite the efforts in Brecknock, continuing losses to gamekeepers and egg collectors, including nest robberies by some individuals supposedly involved in protecting Kites, led to the cessation of breeding in the county by 1909. There were similar problems in other counties, including north Radnor, where Kites faced an additional threat. Here, nestlings taken from local nests were reared in captivity and offered for sale to travellers on the stagecoach to Aberystwyth. There was an apparently lively trade in nestlings in several areas and each bird was reputedly worth between one and five guineas. One nestling was even reported to have been exchanged for a bicycle in the late 1800s (Peter Davis in litt).

In 1903 the highly respected British Ornithologists' Club became involved in Kite protection, passing a motion of censure on any member found to be involved in taking Kite eggs, and helping to set up the first official 'Kite Committee'. Although the details are rather sketchy, it is thought that around this time, the Royal Society for the Protection of Birds (RSPB) also became involved for the first time, donating money to a Kite Preservation Fund so that bounties could be paid, and helping to organise an influential Kite Watchers' Committee.

During such a critical period, with the population reduced to a mere handful of pairs, every breeding failure increased the chance that the Kite would be lost completely. It is therefore hard to understand how, in 1911, George Bolam, a well-known ornithologist but also a dedicated egg collector, came to be appointed as a paid Kite Watcher in Wales, taking over from the influential Edmundes Owen. In the short period that Bolam held this position it is thought, though never proved, that he took several clutches of eggs, before suspicions were aroused and he was relieved of his position.

Many years later, in 1937, another paid Watcher was found to have written to a Guildford egg collector, offering him a clutch of three eggs for £8, in what was probably not an isolated occurrence. Even harder to understand was an incident involving the respected ornithologist Desmond Nethersole-Thompson in 1930. He not only took a clutch of Welsh Kite eggs from the Tywi valley but, a year later, openly exhibited them at a meeting of the British Oological Association causing a storm of protest and even resignations from members appalled by such an action.

Early reintroduction attempts

In East Radnorshire, close to the border with England, the period between the late 1920s and the mid-1940s produced reports of considerable numbers of Kites and rumours of several nests. It was first thought that this represented a welcome expansion of the native population into a new area but now seems most likely to have been the result of an early reintroduction attempt, carried out by C.H. Gowland, an egg-dealer from Liverpool (Davis 1993). Gowland imported batches of Kite eggs from Spain in 1927-28 and again in 1934-35 and had them placed in Buzzard nests in the Builth Wells area (Gowland 1947). Unfortunately, although the nests reportedly produced many fledged young, no systematic records were kept and there is no indication of subsequent survival rates. It would certainly have been interesting to know how the young fared in the wild having been reared to independence by adults of another species. In any event, there is no evidence that any of this Spanish stock recruited into the native population and the Radnor records petered out during the 1940s (Davis 1993).

Capt H.A. Gilbert made a further reintroduction attempt in 1956, this time by placing a single clutch of Spanish eggs in a Radnorshire Buzzard nest. The clutch of three eggs apparently failed to hatch but, undeterred, Gilbert arranged for two young Spanish Kites to be imported later in the year and two more in the following year. On each occasion the young were kept in captivity until the following summer before being released. Once more, there appears to have been no systematic monitoring of the releases although the young birds are reported to have remained in the area for at least a few months before disappearing. Well-monitored releases in England and Scotland undertaken as part of an ongoing reintroduction programme (Chapter 5) have shown that released Kites fare better in the wild if held in captivity for as short a period as possible. It is perhaps unlikely that Gilbert's birds, held in aviaries for approximately one year, survived for long enough to join the Welsh breeding population.

The road to recovery

The Second World War seems to have marked a turning point in the Kite's fortunes, probably helped by wartime travel restrictions limiting the potential for interference with nests, and a reduction in persecution while gamekeepers were away fighting. Although, for the same reasons, there is an incomplete picture of the population size during the war years, by the end of the 1940s it was clear that Kites were breeding in new areas away from the small core population in the Tywi valley. By the early 1950s the breeding population had crept above ten pairs and ten or more young were fledged in most years. There is a suggestion that the outbreak of myxomatosis in 1954 had an adverse effect by reducing the number of Rabbits, one of the Kites' main food sources. Although the number of breeding pairs remained above ten during the second half of the 1950s, breeding success was poor and far fewer young were fledged.

During the 1960s an informal Kite group led by Capt H.R.H. Vaughan oversaw a steady increase in numbers to 27 known pairs by the time a new official Kite Committee met for the first time in 1971. The RSPB and Nature Conservancy Council (NCC) were instrumental in forming the Committee and were able to provide increased resources for protection, monitoring and research. A few years earlier the RSPB had demonstrated its commitment to preserving Kites by purchasing substantial areas of land used by breeding pairs within the Tywi valley.

There were to be further setbacks during the next three decades but, in general, a steady increase in numbers has been maintained right up to the present day. In recent years the rate of population growth has increased, probably as a result of Kites moving into areas of more fertile countryside where breeding productivity is higher, and because of a reduction in illegal persecution.

Into the 21st century

By the mid-1990s, the Welsh population had increased to well over 100 breeding pairs and Kites enjoyed an increasingly high public profile. 'Kite Country', an eco-tourism initiative funded by local authorities and the European Union, was set up in 1994 and was soon helping to attract large numbers of visitors to mid-Wales to see Kites. As part of the initiative, visitor centres were established, some with live video-links to nests during the breeding season. Public viewing facilities were also set up and now attract anything up to 100 Kites by providing food at the same time each day. For a small payment, visitors can now enjoy superb close up views of Kites, not to mention Buzzards and Ravens, from purpose-built hides. Public viewing facilities have also been set up in northern Scotland, where the Kite has been successfully reintroduced, under the banner of 'Highland Red Kite Country'. There is a Red Kite route that can be followed by car and live CCTV pictures from a nest can be viewed, in season, at the North Kessock Tourist Information Centre near Kessock Bridge, Inverness.

The downside of the success story in Wales has been a reduction in funding for the conservation and monitoring of a species no longer seen as such a high priority for limited funds. The RSPB and Countryside Council for Wales (formerly the NCC) reluctantly concluded that the money formerly spent on monitoring Kites in Wales was needed elsewhere. The Kite Country initiative certainly generates considerable income but this goes directly to those involved in the eco-tourism industry rather than to funding the conservation or monitoring of Kites in Wales. Many people felt that the reduction in funding for monitoring work was a little premature, particularly at a time when so many more visitors were coming to mid-Wales, and the potential for disturbance was increasing.

There was also a feeling that the detailed, long-term monitoring of the population, a unique and valuable record of a rare species recovering from the brink of extinction, should be maintained for as long as possible.

As a result of such concerns the Welsh Kite Trust, a registered charity, was set up in 1996 by a group of individuals with a long history of involvement in Kite conservation. Peter Davis, one of the five trustees, has been responsible for keeping detailed records of the Welsh population since 1971 and has been able to maintain this role thanks to the Trust.

England and Scotland

During the 20th century the Kite has become an increasingly regular visitor to England and, to a lesser extent, Scotland, particularly in eastern counties. Records involve a combination of displaced Continental migrants and dispersing young from both the Continent and from central Wales. The pattern of steady increase is well shown by the historical records for Sussex (see Figure 1). It is thought that the Kite ceased to breed in the county sometime before 1825 and from then until the early 1970s the species was only a very scarce and irregular visitor. Only 18 birds were seen during the 94 years between 1843 and 1937, and there were then only three records in the following 24 years to 1961. From the late 1960s the number of records increased and the species became an annual visitor to the county. By the late 1980s as many as nine birds were recorded during a single year (1988), three times the number during the whole of the 1950s and '60s (Hope 1996).

Figure 1: **Annual totals of Red Kites in Sussex, 1962-94 (from Hope 1996)**

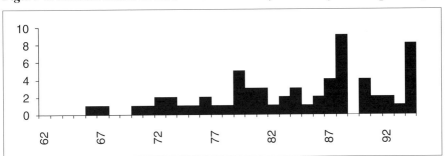

In Norfolk the change in status during the past 150 years has been even more dramatic. The last record in the 19th century was of a single bird shot at Winterton in 1881 and now displayed in the Castle Museum, Norwich. It took a further 77 years for the species to be recorded again in the county, when, in 1958, three singles were seen. There was then a sustained increase during the next few decades with 16 birds in the 1960s, 34 in the 1970s and 43 in the 1980s. The increase continued into the 1990s when wandering birds from the reintroduced populations contributed to the numbers recorded. In the spring of 1996 alone a glut of sightings was thought to have involved about 45 different individuals (Lockwood 1999).

Inland counties too have seen a noticeable increase in records over the last few decades, although the numbers involved are far fewer than for eastern and southern coastal counties.

There are two main reasons for the dramatic increase in records during the last few decades. Firstly, there have been substantial increases in Kite breeding populations, both in mid-Wales and in central and northern Europe, from where the majority of wandering birds or displaced migrants originate. Secondly, there has been a rapid increase in the popularity of birdwatching since the early 1960s and, with more observers on the ground, more of the birds that wander from their breeding areas are likely to be recorded.

Despite the increasing number of records there have been very few occasions where breeding is thought to have taken place away from the known population in central Wales. Young Kites, while prone to wander during their first year, usually return to their natal area when old enough to breed and, as with many other birds of prey, the Kite has shown a great reluctance to recolonise its former range. There have, however, been a few isolated records of pairs apparently settled on a territory in the spring. In 1913, a pair was rumoured to have bred in Devon, and, 64 years later, in 1977, a potential breeding pair was found in Cumbria. This pair was present during the spring of that year, although it is not known whether breeding actually took place. More recently, a pair thought most likely to have originated from central or northern Europe bred successfully in northeast Suffolk in 1996 and 1997 (Carter 1998). These breeding attempts have, in all cases, proved to be isolated occurrences rather than the beginning of natural recolonisation. The Kite has now returned to parts of its former range in England and Scotland as a result of the translocation of young from areas of Europe where the species is still common. The full story of this, one of the most successful bird reintroduction programmes anywhere in the world, is told in Chapter 5.

Chapter 3

BREEDING DISTRIBUTION AND STATUS

The Red Kite's breeding range is almost entirely restricted to Europe, with only small populations found in North Africa, and possibly also in the Cape Verde Islands and parts of the Middle East. From the 19th century or earlier, there was a steady decline across much of the range as a direct result of persecution. The Kite has suffered more than most birds of prey at the hands of man because its association with human habitation, lack of fear of people and scavenging habits make it an easy bird to kill. In some countries, or regions within countries, Kites were reduced to very low levels or wiped out completely, as was the case in England and Scotland. The Kite's adaptability meant that it still thrived in areas where persecution levels were low but the total population was much reduced and the range fragmented.

The decline has continued during the latter part of the 20th century in some areas, particularly in southern and eastern Europe where persecution remains a serious problem. More encouragingly, in parts of central and north-western Europe, there have been population increases and the Kite has regained some of its former range. Denmark, Belgium, the Czech Republic and Austria have all been recolonised during 1970-1990 (Tucker & Heath 1994) and, as a result of a reintroduction programme, Kites are now once again breeding in England and Scotland.

The rest of this chapter provides more details on breeding status and distribution throughout the Kite's range. The information is based on a review by Evans and Pienkowski (1991), augmented with more recent information where available.

Figure 2: **World range of the Red Kite**

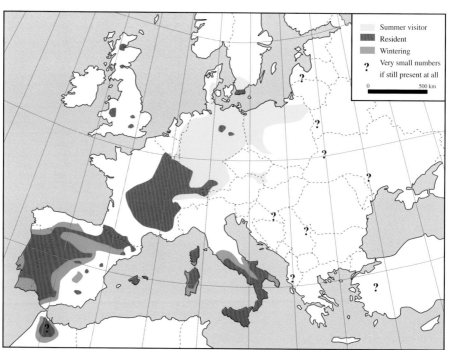

Table 2: **Breeding population and trends**

Country/Island	Estimated number of breeding pairs	Trend in 1990s (if known)	Sources
Austria	10-15 (mid-1990s) 3-5 (1999)	Decline following increase	Gamauf (1995); Andreas Ranner (pers comm.)
Belarus	<10 (1990)	Decline	Tucker & Heath (1994)
Belgium	50-60 (mid-1990s)	Increase	Snow & Perrins (1998)
Canary Islands	Extinct (by early 1970s)		Blanco & González (1992)
Cape Verde Islands	5-6 individuals (1996-97)	Decline	Hille (1998)
Corsica	100-180 (late 1980s)	Stable/Increase	Patrimonio (1990)
Czech Republic	30-50 (1993-94)	Increase	Snow & Perrins (1998)
Denmark	21 (1998)	Increase	Sharrock & Davies (2000)
England	131 (2000)	Increase	English Nature/RSPB
France	2,300-2,900 (1982); 2,250-4,200 (mid-1990s)	Stable/Decline	Thiollay & Terrasse (1984); Viñuela (1996); Rocamora & Yeatmann-Berthelot (1999)
Germany	9,000-12,000 (1999)	Decline	Nicolai (1997); Tucker & Heath (1994); Mebs (1995); Mammen & Opitz (2000)
Hungary	1+ (late 1990s)		Szabolcs Kókay (pers comm.)
Italy	220-250 (late 1990s)	Increase	Corso *et al* (in prep)
Latvia	<3 (late 1980s)	Decline	Evans & Pienkowski (1991); Tucker & Heath (1994)
Lithuania	<3 (late 1980s)	Decline?	Evans & Pienkowski (1991); Tucker & Heath (1994)
Luxembourg	46 (territorial pairs) (1997)	Increase	Conzemius (1998)
Mallorca	27 (mid-1990s)	Decline	Viñuela, Martí & Ruiz (1999)
Menorca	8 (1998)	Decline	Viñuela, Martí & Ruiz (1999)
Moldova	1 (1990)		Tucker & Heath (1994)
Morocco	10-100 (early 1980s)	Decline?	Snow & Perrins (1998)
Netherlands	<5 (late 1990s)	Increase	Van den Berg & Bosman (1999)
Poland	400-500 (early 1990s) 650-700 (late 1990s)	Increase	Adamski (1995); Pawel Brzek (pers comm.)
Portugal	100-200 (mid-1990s)	Stable?	Viñuela (1996)
Rumania	1-10 (early 1990s) 15-20 (1995)	Increase?	Snow & Perrins (1998); Tucker & Heath (1994); Viñuela (1996)
Scotland	39 (2000)	Increase	Scottish Natural Heritage/ RSPB
Slovakia	10-20 (early 1990s)	Decline	Snow & Perrins (1998); Tucker & Heath (1994)

Table 2: **Breeding population and trends** *(continued)*

Country/Island	Estimated number of breeding pairs	Trend in 1990s (if known)	Sources
Spain	3,328-4,044 (1994)	Decline	Viñuela, Martí & Ruiz (1999)
Sweden	850 (1999)	Increase	Kjellén (1999); Kjellén (pers comm.)
Switzerland	300-400 (early 1990s) 800-1,000 (mid-1990s)	Increase	Müller (1995); Schmid *et al* (1998)
Ukraine	5-8 (1990)	Decline	Viñuela (1994)
Wales	259 (2000)	Increase	Welsh Kite Trust
Yugoslavia (former)	<10	Decline	Snow & Perrins (1998)
Total	**18,240-24,240**	**Stable?**	

Britain and Ireland

The long-term decline, leading to extinction in England and Scotland, and reduction to only a handful of pairs in mid-Wales, was described in detail in the previous chapter. The Welsh population has increased slowly but steadily since the 1950s and, in 2000, a survey coordinated by the Welsh Kite Trust estimated the population at 259 breeding pairs.

A reintroduction programme started in England and Scotland in 1989, and, as a result, small populations are now established in four release areas, two each in England and Scotland. The estimated 2000 populations were as follows:

Release area	Breeding pairs
Southern England:	112
Central England:	16
Central Scotland:	7
Northern Scotland:	32

Despite the success of the programme, there has been only limited expansion of range away from the release areas and the vast majority of suitable habitat remains uncolonised. In an attempt to speed up the recolonisation process, releases started at a site in the north of England in 1999 and will continue until at least 2002. There are also plans for a further release project in southern Scotland which is due to begin in 2001.

A pair of Kites that bred successfully in northeast Suffolk in 1996 and 1997 probably involved Continental migrants rather than wandering birds from the reintroduction programme (Carter 1998). It was hoped that a small population would become established in this area but all five of the young reared during the two years dispersed and there have been no further breeding attempts since 1997.

It has been estimated that if the breeding densities currently found in southern England were to be replicated throughout lowland England then the total English population alone would exceed 20,000 pairs (Carter & Grice 2000), about the level of the current world population. While this figure is clearly some way off, given the currently small populations, there is no reason to suppose that it will not be achieved at some point in the future.

Evidence has recently come to light suggesting that the Kite was formerly present in Ireland (D'Arcy 1999), although, as a result of persecution and the early clearance of forests, it was probably wiped out before the time when bird records were routinely kept. A pair was present in the summer of 1976 but apparently did not nest (Cramp & Simmons 1980). The Kite is now a regular visitor to Ireland, mainly as a result of dispersive movements by reintroduced birds from Scotland.

Central Europe

When the majority of Europe was covered with dense forest there would have been few opportunities for the Kite, dependent as it is on open country. The increasing importance of agriculture helped to create a more suitable mixed land-scape of open fields and woodland and, by the early 1800s, the Kite was common and widespread across central Europe. Intense human persecution, particularly between 1850 and 1900, reduced numbers considerably, before protective legis-lation and changing attitudes led to a recovery (Ortlieb 1989).

A census of wintering Kites in Spain provides a rough indication of the number of breeding pairs in central Europe, the region from which Spain's wintering population is largely derived (Viñuela, Martí & Ruiz 1999). The census estimated that, in 1993/94, 54,000-62,000 birds wintered in Spain, in addition to the resident Spanish birds. Allowing for an average of 1.5 young for each breeding pair, this suggests a migratory European population of around 15,500-18,000 pairs, a figure worth bearing in mind when considering the range of estimates for individual European countries below and in Table 2.

Germany is by far the single most important country for breeding Red Kites. Recent estimates range from 9,000-12,000 pairs (Mammen & Opitz 2000) and although this is far lower than some earlier, and almost certainly exaggerated, estimates of up to 25,000 pairs, it still represents about half of the total world population. There have been increases in some areas during the 1990s, but there have also been some worrying declines, particularly in the higher density parts of the breeding range. Declines have been blamed mainly on the intensification of farming methods following the entry of the former East Germany into the European Union (Nicolai 1997) but improvements in waste disposal methods and problems with poisoning of wintering birds in Spain may also be significant factors.

A healthy population in Switzerland at the end of the 19th century declined during the next 50 years until breeding was more or less confined to the Jura mountains. A breeding census in 1969 estimated the population at 90 pairs, rising to 235-300 pairs by the mid-1980s. By the early 1990s the population had increased further to an estimated 300-400 pairs, and occupied a range four times the size of that 25 years previously (Müller 1995; Mosimann & Juillard 1988). This dramatic rate of increase has been maintained and Schmid *et al* (1998) estimated that by the mid-1990s the population had reached 800-1,000 pairs.

Austria also once supported a healthy breeding population but this was lost as a result of intense persecution, mainly during the 19th century. Following a complete absence of breeding records in the 1950s and 1960s, recolonisation took place, probably as a result of immigration from Germany or Switzerland. There was a fairly slow increase to 10-15 pairs in the mid-1990s, concentrated along the Danube, March and Thaya rivers (Gamauf 1995). In more recent years, the population has declined once more, probably as a result of persecution by hunters, and there are now thought to be only 3-5 pairs remaining (Andreas Ranner pers comm.).

The Czech Republic is another central European country that has been recolonised in the recent past. By 1993/94 the population had increased to 30-50 pairs (Snow & Perrins 1998).

Scandinavia

Norway supported a very small population up until about 1880, in the far southeast of the country, close to the border with Sweden. Since then, the Kite has been only a rare visitor, with about 3-4 records annually in recent years, probably birds dispersing from the expanding populations in Sweden and Denmark.

Human persecution reduced the number of Kites in Sweden to below 50 pairs during the 1960s. Since then, the population has increased steadily to an estimated 850 pairs in 1999 (Kjellén pers comm.). The birds are concentrated in the province of Scania but have recently spread into neighbouring Halland and Blekinge. Productivity has remained high despite the increasing numbers and resulting higher breeding densities.

The formerly large Danish population was persecuted to extinction by 1900, although occasional breeding attempts occurred during the next 70 years. In the 1970s the species became a regular breeder once again and, by 1998, the population had increased to 21 breeding pairs, concentrated in southeast Jutland (Jørgensen 1989; Sharrock & Davies 2000).

Northwest Europe

A survey carried out between 1979 and 1982 estimated that there were between 2,300 and 2,900 breeding pairs in France, the third largest country total after Germany and Spain (Thiollay & Terrasse 1984). The main breeding areas were as follows:

Region	Breeding pairs
Lorraine:	740-790
Franche-Comté:	400
Champagne-Ardenne:	480-550
Midi-Pyrénés:	800-1,000

Smaller numbers were found in the Massif Central, Auvergne and Burgundy. Overall, the population is thought to have remained stable or increased slightly in the period 1970-90, but there have been some worrying recent decreases in parts of the range. Over 50% of the breeding population has been lost in Alsace and losses are apparently even greater in Lorraine, Champagne-Ardenne, the Upper Loire Valley and Franche-Comté (J.M. Thiollay in litt; Rocamora & Yeatmann-Berthelot 1999). These losses have been attributed to a variety of causes including habitat loss, severe winter weather, a decline in the number of refuse dumps, and persecution. Poisoning is probably the major threat and Kites are affected by both legal poisoning campaigns carried out to control plagues of voles, and illegal poison baits put out in order to control predatory birds and mammals.

In Belgium, regular breeding ceased in the 1920s and did not resume until 1973. The population increased to 15-20 pairs during the 1980s with the majority of pairs in the east and southeast, and only sporadic breeding elsewhere. By the mid-1990s the population was estimated at 50-60 pairs (Snow & Perrins 1998).

The Luxembourg population increased slowly from the 1940s to an average of about 12-15 pairs during the 1980s, and a maximum of 20 pairs in any one year. It was thought that this might represent the upper limit for the population but, by 1997, the range in the north had expanded and the country as a whole supported 46 territories (Conzemius 1998).

The Netherlands is on the north-western fringe of the Kite's range in continental Europe. There were no confirmed breeding records between 1852 and 1976 but low numbers of pairs are now regularly present in the south and east, having recolonised from neighbouring Germany (Van den Berg & Bosman 1999).

Eastern Europe

In Poland, following a rapid decrease in the 19th and early 20th centuries, there has been a recent recovery, paralleling the increases in adjacent central European countries. In the early 1990s there were an estimated 400-500 pairs and the breeding range was still expanding. The north and west of the country supports the majority of pairs and the Kite is still scarce in central and eastern areas (Adamski 1995). A more recent population estimate suggests that, by the end of the 1990s, there were up to 700 pairs in the country (Pawel Brzek pers comm.).

In contrast, Slovakia has seen a marked decrease in numbers during recent decades with the population in the early 1990s estimated at no more than 10-20 pairs (Snow & Perrins 1998; Tucker & Heath 1994).

The Kite is mainly a rare visitor to Hungary and in recent years only a single breeding pair has been located, in the south of the country (Szabolcs Kókay pers comm.). In neighbouring Rumania an estimated 15-20 pairs were present in the mid-1990s (Snow & Perrins 1998). There have been no proven breeding records for Bulgaria since the 1960s. A long-term decline has taken place in the former Yugoslavia where the species was formerly widely distributed in the north and in Macedonia. A few pairs may still breed in Croatia (Snow & Perrins 1998).

In the former Soviet Union only very limited information on status is available compared with most of the rest of Europe. The Baltic Republics of Latvia and Lithuania may support one or two pairs each, while in Estonia the Kite is only an occasional visitor. Further south, in Belarus, the first confirmed breeding records since the 1950s occurred in 1985 and 1994 (Anon 1996), although the population had been estimated at up to 10 pairs in 1990. Ukraine supported approximately 5-8 pairs in 1990 and neighbouring Moldova just a single pair in the same year. Only a few isolated pairs are thought to survive on the eastern seaboard of the Black Sea in Georgia and Russia. In the former USSR as a whole the total population is probably less than 100 pairs (Snow & Perrins 1998).

Iberia and the Balearic Islands

Spain is second only to Germany in terms of the size of its breeding population. In common with Germany there has been considerable variation in estimates of population size, ranging from as few as 1,000 to as many as 10,000 pairs in the 1980s (Cramp & Simmons 1980; Meyburg & Meyburg 1987). During 1994, the first full national census, carried out using both road-transect counts and counts of breeding territories, gave an estimate of 3,328-4,044 pairs (Viñuela, Martí & Ruiz 1999). The distribution was found to be patchy with some provinces in western and central Spain supporting densities as high as those commonly found in central Europe, but other areas with only low densities or no Kites at all. Overall, the population has declined in recent decades and in only a few areas are populations stable or increasing.

Viñuela, Martí and Ruiz (1999) blamed the declines in Spain on the two main problems affecting Spanish raptors generally – persecution (particularly poisoning and shooting) and, to a lesser extent, electrocution by power lines. They also thought that reductions in extensive livestock farming and competition with Black Kites might have had adverse effects in some areas.

There have been alarming declines in the number of Kites on the two Balearic Islands of Mallorca and Menorca. In Mallorca, the Kite was fairly common until the 1950s, before suffering a drastic reduction to only 27 pairs. In Menorca the situation is even worse. A population estimated at 135 pairs in the late 1980s crashed to only eight pairs by 1998. On both islands the declines have been attributed to poisoning and electrocution by powerlines (Viñuela, Martí & Ruiz 1999).

The Red Kite has been one of the most heavily persecuted raptors in Portugal, leading to a marked decline over recent decades. By the mid-1980s, the population seemed to have stabilised at around 100-200 pairs, which is the approximate level of more recent estimates (Rufino, Araüjo & Abreu 1985; Viñuela 1996).

Central and eastern Mediterranean

In Italy, a long-term decline appears to have been halted, and population estimates have increased from 110-140 pairs in the early 1990s (Viñuela 1996) to 220-250 pairs in the late 1990s (Corso *et al* in prep). Persecution, in the form of poisoning, and interference at nests remain serious problems in some areas. The islands of Sicily and Sardinia were formerly strongholds but numbers have fallen rapidly during the last 20 years. The decline has been particularly dramatic in Sicily where a population of 70-100 pairs has been reduced to only 12-14 pairs as a result of poisoning and interference with nests (Snow & Perrins 1998).

Corsica supports a relatively stable population of 100-180 pairs (Patrimonio 1990) despite the threat posed by the use of strychnine baits to control Foxes. Increases in Rabbits since their introduction in the late 1970s are thought to have benefited Kites, and this is now the main prey species in parts of the island (Mougeot 2000).

Canary Islands

It is thought that the Kite became extinct on the islands in the late 1960s or early 1970s and the species is now only an irregular and uncommon visitor (Blanco & González 1992; Snow & Perrins 1998).

Cape Verde Islands

There has been much confusion regarding the status of the Cape Verde Kite. The predominant view is that this bird represents a distinct subspecies of the Red Kite, *Milvus milvus fasciicauda*, with characteristics intermediate between those of the Black Kite, and the European race of Red Kite. Some authorities consider that these birds are hybrids between the two species, while others have suggested that they may even represent a subspecies of the Black Kite. Hazevoet (1995) examined 32 birds from the islands initially identified as Red Kites. He classed 25 as pure *fasciicauda*, six as Black Kites and one as a hybrid. Genetic studies may provide more information on the true relationship between *fasciicauda*, the various races of Black Kite and the nominate race of Red Kite.

Hybridisation with Black Kites is one of the factors that has been blamed for the decline of the Cape Verde Kite which, up until the 1950s, was much more widespread in the islands. By the early 1990s small populations were thought to remain only on the islands of Santiago and Santo Antão, with perhaps up to 50-75 pairs in total (Snow & Perrins 1998). A study by Hille (1998) carried out in 1996-97 revealed that the sharp decline had continued. The total population was estimated at only 5-6 individuals on the western-most island of Santo Antão and there was no evidence of breeding. Black Kite numbers had also declined dramatically. Possible reasons put forward to explain these alarming declines include human persecution, an increase in aridity on the islands, pressure from human activities and overgrazing by livestock.

North Africa and the Middle East

The Kite is now very scarce in North Africa and there has been no recent proof of breeding. The largest population in recent times was in Morocco where 10-100 pairs were present in the early 1980s (Snow & Perrins 1998). There has since been a marked decline with no proven records in recent years. However, the main breeding areas in the Rif and Middle Atlas mountains in northern Morocco are not well monitored and it is quite possible that a small breeding population remains. Algeria and Tunisia formerly supported small populations but Kites are now only seen in small numbers during the winter. It is thought that the Kite may breed in very small numbers in Turkey, Iran and Iraq but there have been no confirmed breeding records from these countries in recent times.

Overall population and status

In the 1980s the Red Kite was considered by the World Conservation Union (IUCN) to be *Globally Threatened* (Collar & Andrew 1988), meaning that unless appropriate action was taken, there was a danger that the species would continue to decline towards extinction. Evans and Pienkowski (1991) considered that the world population was only 11,000-13,000 pairs, but increases in parts of northwest and central Europe, and an upward revision of the population estimate for Germany, led to much higher estimates in the 1990s. Tucker and Heath (1994) thought that there were between 19,000 and 37,000 pairs of Kites in Europe, with the large range reflecting the lack of an accurate population estimate for some countries, including Germany. Although the species is no longer considered to be *Globally Threatened* it was listed in 'Birds in Europe: Their Conservation Status' as a *Species of European Conservation Concern* because of its restricted world range.

It is difficult to get an accurate impression of the Kite's current status because the recent fortunes of the species have varied dramatically in different parts of the range, even, in some cases, within individual countries. In Germany, Spain and France, the three countries supporting the largest number of pairs, there have been local increases during the latter half of the 1990s, but the majority of populations within these countries have been in decline, particularly in the highest density parts of the range. However, in Switzerland, Sweden and Poland, numbers have risen dramatically during the last decade, making these countries, respectively, the 4th, 5th and 6th most important for the species. The review carried out for this book has resulted in an estimate for the total world population of 18,240-24,240 pairs (see Table 2). The relatively narrow range reflects an improved knowledge of breeding numbers in most countries, particularly Germany, where previous estimates had ranged from 11,000 to as many as 25,000 pairs.

The world Kite population is put into perspective by considering the similar sized Buzzard. Taylor, Hudson and Horne (1988) estimated that, despite the continued absence of this species from much suitable habitat in central and eastern parts of the country, there were between 12,000 and 17,000 pairs in Britain. The upper end of this estimate is not far short of the conservative estimate for the total world population of the Red Kite. The European Buzzard population (including Russia) was estimated by Bijlsma (1997) as 903,000 pairs, making it approximately 45 times as numerous as the Red Kite.

Overall, the worrying declines in parts of the Kite's core range are probably balanced by increases in other areas and total numbers are thought to be roughly stable. Even so, large parts of the Kite's historical range have yet to be recolonised and other areas support far lower densities than was the case in the past. The total population remains well below the level that might be expected were it not for the adverse effects of persecution during the last two centuries.

Chapter 4

MIGRATION AND WINTERING

The Red Kite shows considerable variation in migratory behaviour in different parts of its range, as is the case with many European birds. Some populations are largely resident and, once an individual has bred for the first time, it may not stray further than a few kilometres from its nest site for the rest of its life. By contrast, the majority of Kites in other populations undertake a prolonged migration between separate breeding and wintering areas each year, amounting to tens of thousands of kilometres during the course of an average lifespan. Displaced migrants are regular in parts of Europe close to the main breeding or wintering areas and there is a small but regular spring passage through coastal counties of southern and eastern Britain, made up largely of Continental birds.

Reasons for migration

It is in northern, central and eastern Europe, where winters are harsh, that the Kite is a mainly migratory species. In these areas, the majority of the population undertakes an annual return journey of 3,000km or more to spend the winter in more temperate climes, mainly in Spain. In Britain, the moderating influence of the maritime climate means that winters are far less severe, and here, as in southern Europe, adult Kites are mainly resident.

There are clearly costs involved in undertaking a long distance migration and, for it to be worthwhile, these must be outweighed by the benefits of wintering in an area with a more temperate climate. Survival during a harsh winter is certainly more difficult than in areas where conditions are less severe. For one thing, more food must be consumed in cold conditions in order to maintain the required body temperature. Moreover, food may be harder to come by, as the diversity of potential prey is likely to decline as other species migrate in order to escape the conditions. Prolonged snow cover is particularly difficult for a species that is so heavily dependent on animal carrion as, once carcasses become covered with snow, they are inaccessible to the Kite with its reliance on keen eyesight to locate food.

Distribution in winter

Iberia supports the bulk of the world Red Kite population in winter, including most of the large breeding population from central Europe. There are no good estimates for the numbers present in Portugal but they are thought to be relatively low and Spain undoubtedly supports the vast majority of the population. A census was carried out in Spain in the winter of 1993/94 using a combination of road transect surveys and counts of birds at communal roost sites (Viñuela, Martí & Ruiz 1999). This estimated the number of wintering birds at 54,000-62,000, in addition to the resident Spanish birds. The distribution of birds was patchy with the southern Pyrenees, Segovia province and western parts of Castilla y León found to be particularly important. Densities varied from 2 birds/km^2 in limited areas to 0-0.5/km^2 across the majority of the range. Some lowland areas of Spain without a breeding population support significant numbers of Red Kites in winter, and it has been suggested that the lack of competition from the migratory Black Kite at this time of year may make such areas more attractive. On a more local scale, the highest densities were found in areas with an abundance of poultry and livestock carrion, an important source of food for wintering Kites in the region. Although some Spanish breeding pairs are sedentary, remaining close to their nest sites throughout the year, others undertake movements within Spain, often joining up with immigrants from central Europe.

Far smaller numbers winter elsewhere in southern Europe. Sagot (1991) estimated that the wintering population in southwest France, close to the western Pyrenees, was around 1,000-1,500 individuals with lower numbers elsewhere in the country. In Italy, surveys carried out in 1997/98 and 1998/99 recorded 850-1,150 wintering Kites, mainly concentrated in central-southern Italy and it was estimated that the total population was up to 1,500 birds (Corso *et al* 1999). Only very low numbers of Kites are believed to overwinter in North Africa but counts at Gibraltar, the main crossing point between south-western Europe and North Africa for many migratory birds of prey, have included up to 200 Kites during the spring and autumn migration periods (Bergier 1987).

Kites ringed in central Europe have provided confirmation that the majority of this population move southwest to wintering grounds as most recoveries have been from Spain, southern Portugal and southern France (Cramp & Simmons 1980). There have also been winter recoveries from Italy, Sardinia and the Balkans, showing that at least a small proportion of the population moves south or southeast to winter in central or eastern parts of the Mediterranean.

Changes in wintering range

Since the late 1950s there has been an increasing tendency for a proportion of the northern and central European population to remain in their breeding areas during the winter (Nicolai 1997). In Sweden, it is thought that this behavioural change may have been prompted by a programme of winter feeding. With a more reliable source of food, the cold winter conditions evidently became easier to withstand and there was less need to undertake a relatively long-distance migration.

In central Europe, overwintering was considered exceptional until the early 1960s but has subsequently become a regular occurrence with substantial numbers attending communal roosts in some areas. One of the largest roosts in eastern Germany held up to 250 birds in November 1994 (George 1995). In Switzerland, wintering was first reported in 1969/70 but has now become regular, with a total population of 400-600 birds at two large and a number of smaller roosts (Müller 1995; Mosimann & Juillard 1988). There is little information on the composition of groups of Kites overwintering in central Europe, although both locally breeding adults and young of the year are known to be present at communal roosts in Germany.

The reason for the change in wintering behaviour is not known for certain but the milder winters (on average) over the last few decades may well have been a significant factor (Snow & Perrins 1998) and an increase in refuse tips is thought to have provided a more reliable source of food. It is interesting that some Black Kites now remain for the winter in Spain rather than undertaking their usual migration to south of the Sahara (Muntaner & Mayol 1996). If global warming leads to a reduction in the severity of winters in central and northern Europe in the coming years then a higher proportion of the Red Kite population may forgo the annual migration. However, in parts of Germany, it has been suggested that recent improvements in waste-disposal methods have reduced food availability in winter, leading to local reductions in the number of birds that remain throughout the year (Evans & Pienkowski 1991).

Viñuela, Martí and Ruiz (1999) thought that short-term changes in weather patterns in central Europe were an important factor in determining how many birds remained during the winter. They noted the considerable inter-annual variation in the number of Kites wintering in Spain and suggested that, in harsh winters, a higher proportion of the population was likely to migrate south from central and northern Europe.

Timing of migration

Some Kites begin to move south towards their wintering areas in late summer as shown by the recovery of a German-ringed bird in southwest France in late August (Cramp & Simmons 1980). Movements begin in earnest, however, in September, and passage through France is at its highest during the second half of September and through October. A long-term study of the autumn migration of Kites through the Pyrenees (Urcun & Bried 1998) found that passage was concentrated at several south facing mountain valleys, particularly at the western end of the range. Between 5,000 and 10,000 birds were recorded in most years with the bulk of the movements in the last week of September and during October, later than the main passage of most other birds of prey in the area. Figure 3 shows the clear difference in the migration periods of Black and Red Kites in the Pyrenees. Black Kites begin to cross south in mid-July and the bulk of the movements are during August. By the end of August only very small numbers are still passing through, well before the start of the main passage of Red Kites. Black Kites have by far the longer migration of the two species as they winter in Africa south of the Sahara desert. They are also less tolerant of cool and damp conditions than Red Kites and both these factors favour a southwards movement as early as possible after the breeding season. In contrast, Red Kites have only a relatively short onward journey into Spain to their wintering areas and they seem better adapted to cope with the cool and damp conditions that are sometimes found in central Europe in late summer. In spring, Black Kites arrive, on average, several weeks later than Red Kites and so must compress their breeding season into a much shorter period (Snow & Perrins 1998).

Figure 3: **Autumn migration of Red and Black Kites across the Pyrenees (from Urcun & Bried 1998)**

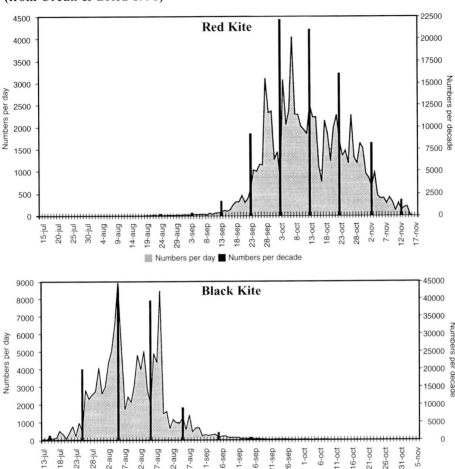

Movements of Red Kites continue across the Pyrenees into November although, by this time, most birds are already settled in their wintering areas. The minority of birds that remain in central Europe for the winter may undertake a southwards movement at almost any time if there is a sustained spell of poor weather, apparently even as late as February, not long before the usual onset of return migration (George 1994).

The majority of Kites arrive back in their breeding areas during March, with northwards movements beginning in about mid-February and continuing into

April and May in northern Europe. Gottschalk (1995) found that birds passing through the Vortaunus region of western Germany between 1984 and 1994 were concentrated into a relatively short period from the last week of February until about mid-March, with only low numbers of passage birds in April and May. It is thought that males generally return to their breeding sites before the females, as is often the case in migratory species.

Migrant Kites in spring tend to be less gregarious than is the case in autumn. In Gottschalk's study, singles and small groups of up to 10-15 birds predominated in spring, whereas in autumn, groups of between 30 and 50 birds were relatively common. Urcun and Bried (1998) recorded flocks of up to 100 birds passing through the Pyrenees in autumn, although the average group size during the peak migration period was only 3-4 birds. There may be greater opportunity for flocking during the more leisurely autumn migration as birds have time to gather together while awaiting suitable conditions for onward migration. In spring, the adults are no doubt keen to return to their breeding areas and re-establish territories as quickly as possible, and are therefore perhaps more willing to continue travelling in adverse conditions.

It is not known whether birds travel in family parties during the autumn migration but juveniles may well benefit from migrating in groups with adults (even if not with their parents), as such individuals have already successfully spent at least one winter in southern Europe. This is perhaps another reason why flocking tends to be more common during the autumn migration.

Displaced migrants

Kite records in Britain away from the main breeding areas involve a combination of migrants from central and northern Europe, and young birds dispersing from the Welsh and, since 1989, reintroduced, populations. Records are most numerous in southern and, particularly, eastern coastal counties and the pattern of records, with a clear peak in spring, suggests that the majority of these birds are displaced migrants on route between wintering areas in Iberia and breeding sites in central or northern Europe. Autumn and winter records are more likely to involve wandering juveniles from within Britain but no doubt also include a small proportion of dispersing Continental birds. The general pattern of occurrence is shown for various counties in Table 3. The spring peak is obvious, with records in March and April accounting for 47% of the annual total. Relatively few birds are seen during the summer months and records then increase again in autumn and winter.

In 1996 there was a particularly impressive spring passage of birds along the English east coast. This was most apparent in Norfolk where the first bird was

Table 3: **Monthly totals[1] of migrant Kites in selected English counties**

County	Jan	Feb	Mar	Apr	May	Jun	Jul	Aug	Sep	Oct	Nov	Dec	Source
Sussex 1962-94	5	2	10	8	6	3	0	4	1	5	8	5	Hope (1996)
Dorset 1950-1996	3	3	8	10	5	3	2	2	2	5	4	4	Morrison (1997)
Hampshire 1956-92	6	3	5	3	1	1	2	3	1	3	4	1	Clark & Eyre (1993)
Norfolk 1973-1988	5	3	38	16	7	1	1	0	0	0	3	13	Norfolk Bird Reports 1973-88
Suffolk 1992-1996	3	7	18	22	2	6	0	4	2	3	2	4	Suffolk Birds 1992-1996
Northumberland 1985-98	1	1	3	9	0	1	0	1	0	2	1	2	Birds in Northumbria 1985-98
Total	**23**	**19**	**82**	**68**	**21**	**15**	**5**	**14**	**6**	**18**	**22**	**29**	

[1] These figures may include some duplicate records where the same bird has been recorded at several different locations

seen on 9th March and, from then until 1st June, an estimated 45 birds were recorded, two more than were seen in the county throughout the whole of the 1980s (Lockwood 1999). It is unlikely that many were wandering birds from the reintroduction programme as none were reported to have wing-tags. In stark contrast to this glut of spring records, a mere two birds were reported in Norfolk during the following autumn.

There is a similar pattern of records on the near Continent where there is also a regular spring passage of Kites, particularly in areas adjacent to significant breeding populations. The Netherlands supports fewer than five breeding pairs but is not far from the large populations in Germany. The main passage is from mid-February to mid-May and this period accounts for, on average, 63% of each year's records (SOVON 1987). The majority of the birds seen early in the spring are adults, presumably keen to return to their breeding sites at the earliest opportunity. In April and May an increasing proportion of the birds are non-breeding immatures. These birds have no breeding site to hurry back to and can therefore afford a more leisurely migration.

A few non-breeding birds remain in the Netherlands throughout the summer and there is then a slight increase in birds seen in the autumn, although involving far lower numbers than in spring. It is not clear why there is such a heavy bias towards spring records in coastal counties of England and on the near Continent. In the Netherlands, the same pattern is apparent for the Black Kite but, for many scarce migrants, autumn records usually outnumber those in spring. This partly

reflects the larger population sizes following the breeding season and is also influenced by the fact that juveniles are less experienced than adults and are more prone to stray from the usual migration route. Perhaps both Red and Black Kites are driven by a strong urge to move south towards the wintering areas in autumn and take a more direct route than is the case in spring.

It is known from ringing recoveries that some immatures from central European breeding grounds remain in the Spanish wintering areas throughout their second calendar year (Cramp & Simmons 1980). These individuals presumably delay the long journey back to the natal area until they are old enough to breed, usually when they are at least two years old.

Vagrants

As a result of the Kite's migratory habits in parts of its range and the tendency for some first-year birds to disperse even in resident populations, vagrants have been recorded from many countries outside the usual range. Snow and Perrins (1998) listed Finland, Malta, Armenia, Cyprus, Lebanon, Israel, Libya, and Madeira as countries where the Kite was a rare visitor and Iceland has recently been added to the list following the arrival of a first-year bird from northern Scotland (see Chapter 10). Even further afield, wandering individuals have been reported from India (Prakash 1989) and Bangladesh (Sarker & Sarker 1985).

Chapter 5

REINTRODUCTION

During the past few decades many different birds of prey have been the subject of reintroduction attempts in a large number of countries across the world. Much of the early work was carried out in the United States where projects to restore populations of Peregrine, Osprey and the highly endangered California Condor commenced in the 1970s and '80s. In Britain the first efforts to reintroduce the White-tailed Eagle in Scotland were made as early as 1959, although a breeding population has only become established as a result of further releases from 1975 to 1998.

Birds of prey feature disproportionately highly in reintroduction projects for reasons connected both to their ecology and to human attitudes towards them. As they are often at the top of the food chain, and occur at relatively low densities, they are especially vulnerable to the adverse effects of human activities, including habitat destruction, pesticide poisoning and direct persecution. This has resulted in the complete loss of some species from large parts of their range. Even if conditions improve, natural recolonisation may be hindered by a slow reproductive rate and the inbuilt tendency for the individuals of many species to breed close to the area where they themselves were born and reared. The young of most birds of prey are relatively easy to maintain in captivity, at least for a short period, and they require only infrequent provisioning with food. In contrast, projects involving small passerines may require complex captive-rearing techniques in order to rear young successfully, including food provisioning many times each day.

Birds of prey are generally popular with the public as a result of their impressive size or spectacular hunting behaviour and conservation organisations find it easier to attract funds for projects involving such high profile species than is the case with other, possibly equally deserving, groups. It is, however, generally accepted that work to restore populations of birds of prey encourages changes in the environment that benefit a wide range of other wildlife. If conditions are suitable for the reintroduction of a top predator then there must be adequate populations of prey species as well as sufficient suitable habitat for breeding and finding food. The factors that caused the loss of the species in the first place must also have been addressed. This could involve educational campaigns to tackle problems of persecution, pesticide poisoning or habitat management, all resulting in knock-on benefits to a wide range of different species.

This chapter concentrates on work with the Red Kite in England and Scotland, describing the background to the reintroduction programme, the methods used and the progress that has been achieved since the first birds were released in 1989. Table 6, at the end of the chapter, provides summary details for other recent projects in Europe involving the reintroduction of birds of prey.

Background to reintroduction in England and Scotland

In the mid-1980s the Red Kite was one of only three species in the United Kingdom considered to be threatened on a global scale, and, as such, was a particularly high priority for conservation. Although the small population in central Wales was recovering from past persecution, the rate of recovery was very slow as a result of the cool, damp climate and unproductive habitat. In 1986, the Nature Conservancy Council (now English Nature in England and Scottish Natural Heritage in Scotland) and the RSPB set up a UK Red Kite Project Team to look at ways in which the fortunes of the species could be improved. After careful consideration, the Project Team decided to embark upon an, initially experimental, project to evaluate reintroduction as a method for restoring Kites to suitable areas throughout England and Scotland.

Reintroduction is not an option that should be undertaken lightly. Projects require a long-term commitment, with sufficient funding to carry out the necessary releases of birds, often over many years, and for a programme of monitoring to detect any problems at an early stage. Internationally agreed criteria for reintroduction projects have been set out by the World Conservation Union (IUCN) (Green 1979), and the experimental Kite project was only given the go ahead when it was certain that it complied with these in full. The following summary, based on the IUCN criteria, shows why the Red Kite was a suitable candidate for reintroduction (see also Evans *et al* 1997; Carter, Evans & Crockford 1995):

- **Historical evidence of former natural occurrence**
Projects involving translocation should normally only seek to restore species that are a natural part of the area's wildlife. In the case of the Red Kite there is good evidence from old avifaunas and other literature that the species was formerly widespread and often abundant in England and Scotland.

- **A clear understanding of the factors causing extinction (and these factors should no longer apply)**
The Kite was wiped out from England and Scotland as a direct result of intensive human persecution. Birds of prey are still persecuted in parts of Britain today, but it was thought highly unlikely that a species harmless to farming and game-rearing interests would be persecuted to such a degree that a reintroduction project would be jeopardised.

- **Suitable habitat available to support the reintroduced population**
Although the countryside has changed dramatically during the 200 years since the Kite was last a familiar sight across Britain, studies of the bird's ecology in Wales and elsewhere in Europe indicated that the majority of the former range in England and Scotland was still suitable. The patchwork of mixed farmland and woodland that is typical of large areas of lowland Britain was thought to provide ideal nesting, roosting and foraging habitats.

- **Natural recolonisation unlikely within a reasonable timescale**
If a species is able to recolonise an area naturally within a reasonable period of time then there is clearly no need for a time consuming and expensive reintroduction project, and the resources should be used on a more

deserving cause. The Welsh Kite population has long been hampered in its recovery by the unsuitable climate and unproductive countryside, and, despite many years of protection and dedicated conservation efforts, there were no signs of the range extending beyond central Wales into more suitable lowland habitat. There were also concerns that the use of poison baits to control corvids and Foxes in the border country of England and Wales might be hindering population expansion.

• A suitable source of birds for release

At the start of the project there were two main options for obtaining Kites for release. The birds could be either bred in captivity or taken from donor populations in the wild. Captive breeding was tried using injured adult birds from Spain that were unfit for release into the wild. This proved to be very difficult and it quickly became clear that, in order to obtain sufficient birds for a large-scale release programme, it would be necessary to take birds from a donor population. Kites are still common in parts of Continental Europe and the authorities in several areas agreed to supply young birds for the programme.

Reintroduction methods

The first phase of the reintroduction programme was carried out over five years at two sites, one in southern England and a second in northern Scotland. These release projects, beginning in 1989, were initially regarded as experimental, the main aim being to establish methods by which Kites could be re-established in the wild. If the projects proved to be successful then they could be repeated elsewhere in order to restore the species to suitable areas throughout Britain. Following the successful establishment of self-sustaining breeding populations at both initial sites, releases were extended to a further three sites – central England starting in 1995, central Scotland in 1996 and northern England in 1999.

Selection of the first two release areas

The majority of lowland Britain is suitable for the Red Kite with its undemanding habitat requirements and generalist diet. Only in urban areas and perhaps in large areas of countryside with few trees, such as the East Anglian fens, would Kites probably struggle to survive. It was nevertheless important that the first two reintroduction attempts were carried out in areas that offered conditions as close as possible to ideal in order to maximise the survival rates of released birds and improve the chances that breeding populations would become established.

The Project Team set out a series of simple criteria for selecting potential areas, based on a knowledge of the Kite's main requirements and causes of mortality in other parts of its range (Lovegrove, Elliot & Smith 1990):

1. There should be a sufficiently large area of suitable habitat and not an isolated patch of good habitat in an otherwise unsuitable area. Good habitat comprises a combination of woodland for nesting and roosting, and mixed farmland, including both grassland and arable crops, to provide foraging areas.
2. The area should support a sustainable food supply in both summer and winter.
3. The breeding success of Buzzards (if present) should be high, indicating a good food supply and a low level of persecution.
4. So far as possible, the area should be free from illegal poison baits.
5. The area should have a low annual rainfall and be below an altitude of 350m above sea level.
6. The local community in the area should be supportive of the project.

The two areas finally selected were the Chiltern Hills in the south of England and the Black Isle in northern Scotland. In both areas a number of landowners were contacted and asked if they would agree to support the project by allowing birds to be released on their estates. Two estates were chosen and preparations began in earnest during 1989 with the construction of large wooden release aviaries at each of the two sites, ready to receive the first young birds later in the year.

Collection of young

Most of the Kites released into the wild have been collected as 4-6 week old nestlings from healthy populations within the European breeding range. The majority of birds for release in England have been collected from central and northern Spain, while those released in Scotland have come from southern Sweden and, more recently, eastern Germany. A small number of the birds released in England were rescued from nests in Wales either as eggs, where the nests were considered to be at risk from egg collectors, or small nestlings that would almost certainly not have survived if left in the nest. These were reared in captivity by Dr Nick Fox using a female Buzzard as a surrogate mother in order to minimise human contact, before being transferred to the release aviaries when 4-6 weeks old. More recently, nestlings have been taken from the expanding reintroduced population in southern England and released at sites in central England and Yorkshire.

Nests from which chicks are collected are always left with at least one nestling so that the adult pair remain at the site with a good chance of breeding successfully. It had been thought that the chick or chicks left in donor nests had an improved chance of survival as, if food were in short supply, their share would increase following the removal of competing siblings (Carter *et al* 1999). However, there is recent evidence from collecting young in southern England that survival rates for individually marked chicks remaining in donor nests are lower than for those in nests that are not manipulated (Peter Stevens in litt). It is not known why this is the case as donor nests are certainly not abandoned by the adults. Perhaps the remaining chick(s) interpret the disappearance of their siblings as predation and therefore try to leave the nest as soon as possible, sometimes before they are able to fly strongly. This could increase the risk of accidents and fledglings that end up on the ground due to poor flying ability become vulnerable to ground predators such as Foxes.

By the time that Kite nestlings reach four weeks of age they are fully feathered and are able to regulate their own body temperature. They no longer require brooding by one of the parent birds during cool or wet weather, and so there is no need to provide an artificial heat source when they are held in captivity as would

Climbing to a nest in central Spain in order to collect nestlings for the reintroduction programme (Ian Carter)

be necessary with younger, downy chicks. Collecting chicks when they are several weeks old also reduces the chance that they will become conditioned to people during their time in captivity. Younger chicks would need to be hand fed as, in the wild, they would have been fed on small pieces of food offered by one of the parent birds. By four weeks, chicks are able to tear food for themselves so hand feeding can be avoided, and the young have a far better chance of adapting to life in the wild when they are released.

Care in captivity

The young Kites spend about 6-8 weeks in captivity, remaining in the aviary at the release site throughout this period. When they first arrive, the chicks are placed, three or four together, on an artificial stick nest in a covered section of the aviary. Food is provided daily on the nest using a small hatch built into each compartment, so that human contact is kept to a minimum. Finding suitable sources of food is relatively easy as a result of the Kite's preference for carrion and their remarkably varied natural diet. Local farmers, gamekeepers and foresters have provided food at some sites in the form of Muntjac, Fallow Deer, Rabbits, Grey Squirrels and corvids, controlled as part of their routine pest management programmes.

Each compartment within the release aviary measures 8×8×20 feet, giving the birds room to exercise and strengthen their flight muscles before release (Ian Carter)

Young Kites from central Spain arriving at the release aviary in central England (Ian Carter)

To provide variation, road casualty birds and mammals have been fed to captive Kites in England and, in northern Scotland, fish heads and offal from a local Salmon processing factory were utilised as a food source.

When the chicks are only 4-5 weeks old, carcasses are chopped into relatively small pieces to ensure that the food is in a form that can be readily ingested. As the chicks grow they quickly become more adept at tearing food for themselves and large pieces of meat or whole carcasses are then provided. The young are provisioned with as much food as they can eat and, as would be expected in a natural situation, the amount required tends to drop once the birds are almost full-grown. At this stage food is required only for body maintenance rather than to fuel growth. As with the majority of birds of prey, Kites derive all the water they need from their food and so it is not necessary to provide captive birds with a source of drinking water.

Perches are provided within each compartment so that when the young birds reach fledging age, at 7-8 weeks, they are able to fly between perches and build up their wing muscles in preparation for their first flights in the wild. Despite their large size, Kites are remarkably manoeuvrable and the young birds quickly learn to turn around in mid-air within the aviaries in order to fly several lengths without stopping to land.

Table 4: **Food supplied to Red Kites reared and released in southern England in 1990 and 1991 (from Evans *et al* 1997)**

	1st Jun – 28th Jul 1990	7th Jun – 10th Aug 1991	25th Jun – 27th Jul 1991
No. of days	58	65	32
No. of young Kites	11	11-15	2
Mallard	–	1	–
Common Pheasant	–	3	–
Woodpigeon	15	22	–
Jay	–	4	0
Magpie	81	41	8
Carrion Crow	56	24	1
Rook	20	–	–
Jackdaw	3	1	1
Stoat	4	4	–
Weasel	4	8	–
Fox	10	3	–
Rabbit	129	125	17
Grey Squirrel	18	136	9

Release by hacking

When the young Kites are 10-12 weeks old they are released in groups by removing a large wooden panel from the front of each aviary compartment. Some fly strongly out over the surrounding countryside and circle over the area for several minutes, as if inspecting their surroundings, before coming to rest. Others quickly perch in a nearby tree after only a short first flight.

In most birds of prey, young remain dependent on their parents for several weeks after leaving the nest. The technique of hacking, whereby food is provided at, or close to, the release site until the birds have adapted to finding their own food in the wild, simulates this period of dependence. There is much variation in the amount of time that released Kites remain dependent on food provided at the aviaries. Some continue to take food for three weeks or more, although they are no doubt also finding alternative sources of food by this stage. Others disperse away from the release area within a few days, and are clearly already fully independent by this stage. The fact that the majority of released Kites do not return to the aviaries to take advantage of handouts for more than a few weeks is, initially, rather surprising. It would seem to make more sense for the young birds to make the most of a guaranteed source of food as long as it remained available. The most likely explanation is that it is unwise for a scavenging bird to rely too heavily on just a single source of food, however reliable it seems to be in the short term. A far safer strategy is to gain a thorough knowledge of the wider area and a range of different places where food sources are present. Then, if one source of food unexpectedly dries up, the birds will already be familiar with alternative sites where food can be obtained. The released Kites seem to follow this strategy and once they are familiar with the local area they have no need to keep returning to the aviaries in order to find food.

Some reintroduction projects involve species that rely on specialised hunting techniques and, as released young are deprived of the opportunity to learn such techniques from their parents, survival rates may be reduced. Although projects involving such species, including Peregrine and Osprey, can be successful (see Table 6), the survival rates of released birds are rarely as high as has been the case during the Red Kite programme. The Kite's preference for animal carrion, food that can be exploited using relatively simple foraging behaviours, means that a lack of contact with the parent birds is not a serious disadvantage.

Monitoring of released birds

All well-planned reintroductions include a programme of monitoring so that the success, or otherwise, of releases can be assessed. In order to improve the chances of keeping track of the released Kites, each individual is fitted with both plastic, coloured wing-tags and a radio-transmitter while still in the aviary. The plastic attachments for the wing-tags become brittle with age and tags often fall off after a few years. They nevertheless provide valuable information on dispersal behaviour and survival during the vital first few years.

The radio-transmitters widely used in the early years of the reintroduction programme were attached to the two central tail feathers and were lost when these feathers were moulted out about one year later. More recently, harness-mounted transmitters, with a battery life of about three years, have been used. Radio-transmitters enable very detailed information to be collected on dispersal distances and direction, home range, habitat use and survival rates. Radio-tracking is also useful when studying other aspects of the Kite's ecology, allowing, for example, the exact location of roosting sites to be pinpointed. The radio-transmitters include a mercury tilt-switch that causes the pulse rate of the radio-signal to change depending on whether the bird is flying (with the tail horizontal) or perched (with the tail vertical). A sustained lack of variation in the signal suggests that the bird has died and radio-tracking can then be used to locate the carcass. This has allowed post-mortems to be carried out on many fresh carcasses and has helped considerably in determining the main causes of mortality for released Kites.

The range of the transmitters varies depending on the nature of the landscape and the activity of the bird. When there is a direct line of sight between the bird and the person with the radio-receiver the range can be anything up to about 80km. This has been exploited by using aerial surveys to search for missing Kites as a wide transect on either side of the aircraft can be scanned. On the ground, the range is often over 10km when a Kite is flying but this is substantially reduced if

Tail-mounted radio-transmitter used to monitor the progress of released Kites (Ian Carter)

the bird is perched low down or is on the ground and there is no direct line of sight between the receiver and the transmitter.

Progress so far

Although the reintroduction was carefully planned and based on methods that had been successful in reintroducing other bird of prey species in Europe and the United States, no-one could be certain how well the first groups of released Kites would fare. There was therefore considerable relief when monitoring showed that the released birds coped well in the wild and a relatively high proportion survived to breeding age.

From 1989 to 1994, a total of 93 young were released at each of the two initial sites. A minimum of 76% of birds in southern England and 51% of birds in northern Scotland survived their first year (Evans *et al* 1999) with survival rates for older birds and for birds that remained in the release area during their first year substantially higher. The first breeding attempt in England was in 1991 and the first successful breeding in both release areas was in 1992. In this year four pairs fledged nine young in southern England and one pair reared a single chick in northern Scotland. By 2000 the populations had increased to an estimated 112 pairs in southern England and 32 pairs in northern Scotland. Both populations are now considered to be self-sustaining and no further releases are planned in either of these two areas. Monitoring will continue in order to assess the rates of population increase and spread to new areas and, as during the last few years, this will include fitting wing-tags to young Kites while they are still in the nest.

In central England a total of 70 birds were released between 1995 and 1998, and by 2000 a population of 16 pairs had already become established. The third English release site is in Yorkshire, on the Harewood Estate just north of Leeds. A total of 42 birds, all from nests in southern England, were released in 1999 and 2000 and successful breeding has already taken place, only one year after the start of the project. In central Scotland, 97 birds, imported from eastern Germany, were released in 1996-2000 and a small breeding population (seven pairs in 2000) is already established. Plans are now well-advanced to release birds at a third Scottish site, in southern Scotland, which would bring the total number of sites to six since the programme began in 1989 (see Figure 4).

The main loss of reintroduced birds has resulted from dispersal away from the release areas, mainly during the first autumn, soon after release, or during the following spring. Some of the dispersing birds subsequently return, but many do not and are assumed to have perished.

Although the reintroduced populations have increased relatively rapidly, they have been slow to spread out and recolonise new areas well away from the release sites. This is partly the result of an inbuilt tendency, often found in birds of prey, for individuals to breed close to their own birth (or release) site, and partly because the countryside is so well suited to Kites that they are able to thrive at high densities and have no need to search out new areas. Only by releasing birds at several sites has it been possible to establish populations in a number of different areas and so improve the prospects for recolonisation of suitable habitats throughout Britain within a reasonable timescale.

Figure 4: **Approximate location of release sites in England and Scotland**

The long-term existence of any species is dependent on its maintaining as wide a distribution as possible. Once populations are fragmented they become more vulnerable to local environmental pressures and so, by helping to restore Kites in England and Scotland, the reintroduction programme is not only helping to restore one of Britain's most impressive birds of prey but is also contributing to the international conservation of the species.

Table 5: **The Red Kite Reintroduction Programme in Britain**

Release area	Year	Number released	Origin of birds	First successful breeding	Number of breeding pairs				
					1992	1994	1996	1998	2000
Chiltern Hills, southern England	1989-1994	93	Mainly northern Spain; 7 from Wales	1992	4	20	37	71	112
Central England	1995-1998	70	35 from central Spain 33 from southern England; 2 from Wales	1997	–	–	1	4	16
Harewood Estate, northern England	1999-ongoing	42 by 2000	Southern England	2000	–	–	–	–	3
Black Isle, northern Scotland	1989-1993	93	Southern Sweden	1992	1	8	16	23	32
Central Scotland	1996-2000	97	Eastern Germany	1998	–	–	–	2	7
Southern Scotland	Proposed 2001-		Northern Scotland; Southern England						

Rehabilitation

Occasionally, released or wild-fledged Kites are found injured and taken into captivity for veterinary treatment. In some cases, birds have only been recovered because they could be located by radio-tracking and they would otherwise undoubtedly have perished from their injuries. When a population is still small, each individual bird is extremely valuable and successful rehabilitation can make an important contribution to a reintroduction project. This was certainly the case for an adult bird found with shotgun injuries in southern England and released back into the wild in central England, following rehabilitation at the Institute of Zoology, London Zoo. This individual was a member of the first pair to attempt to breed in the area, in the year following release, and has since bred successfully at least three times, helping to rear no fewer than seven young. Another adult bird, again from southern England, was found in very poor condition by a member of the public and, following a period of recuperation in captivity, was released in Yorkshire at the start of the new project in 1999. In 2000, it paired up with a first-year bird and bred successfully, helping to rear the first two young in northern England for well over one hundred years.

Reading wing-tags

Wing-tags are fitted not only to released birds but also to a proportion of wild-fledged young. They may be read on a perched bird at close range with binoculars and at up to about 800m away, in good light conditions, using a telescope. Only by recording the tag colours together with the number, letter or symbol marked on the tag can an individual bird be identified. By simply recording the colour of the tag on each wing it is at least possible to find out from which of the release areas a bird originated and in which year it was released or fledged. The colour of the tag on the left wing indicates the area (yellow – southern England; white – central England; orange – northern England; red – central Scotland; blue – northern Scotland) and the colour of the right wing-tag indicates the year (green – 1998; black – 1999; pink – 2000; blue – 2001).

Reintroduction in Italy

A project to reintroduce the Red Kite to the 'Tocchi' State Natural Reserve in Tuscany, central Italy began in 1995, led by the National Forest Service (Allavena *et al* 1996). Kites were once common in the area but were wiped out by persecution, mainly shooting and poisoning, during the 1960s. The habitat remained suitable and, as a result of a considerable reduction in the use of poisoned baits, it was thought that the area could, once again, support a viable population.

Unlike the programme in England and Scotland, releases involved rehabilitated Kites, donated by the authorities in Spain, rather than nestlings taken from the wild. The first five birds were released in June 1996 following a period of nine months spent in aviaries at the release site. Although some birds had to be recaptured because they were unable to fly properly, others were ranging up to 4-5km away from the aviaries one month after release. Food was provided close to the release site and the birds continued to return to the aviaries in late afternoon to roost. It is not thought that any of the birds survived for long enough to begin breeding in the wild. Kites still breed in Laxio, the neighbouring region to Tuscany, and there are some conservationists in Italy who believe efforts should be focussed on protecting this population effectively, rather than trying to reintroduce birds nearby.

Raptor reintroductions in Europe

Table 6 shows the wide variety of reintroduction projects, involving at least ten different species of bird of prey (in addition to the Red Kite), that have taken place, or are currently taking place, in Europe. The majority of projects have been based upon the hacking of young birds, either bred in captivity or collected from the wild. With many species, the use of young birds collected from suitable donor populations in the wild is the more straightforward option as captive breeding requires considerable expertise and is time consuming and relatively expensive. The use of wild-taken young also carries a reduced risk that the birds will become imprinted on humans, as the young spend the critical first few weeks of life being reared naturally in the wild and spend only a short period of time in captivity before they are released. Most projects involving species that still have healthy wild populations remaining in parts of Europe have used this approach.

Projects involving the three species of vulture have utilised captive-bred birds, mainly because these species became so rare in the wild that collecting sufficient young for a reintroduction programme was not a sustainable option. This was particularly true with the Bearded Vulture (Lammergeier) project in the Alps. By setting up a captive breeding programme involving a number of facilities across Europe it has been possible to release more than 80 birds into the wild. This compares with a total European breeding population estimated at only 86 pairs (Heredia 1997). Projects involving the Peregrine have also relied on captive-bred birds as the long history of captive breeding by falconers ensured a ready source of birds for release into the wild.

Young birds in the wild must make the transition from dependence on their parents to surviving on their own and at this age they seem to be pre-programmed to learn how to find food and to fend for themselves. Reintroduction projects benefit from releasing birds that are close to their natural fledging age, as full advantage is taken of this stage in their development and, as a result, survival rates are often high. Older birds are much more difficult to collect from wild populations and captive-reared adults may find it more difficult to adapt to life in the wild having been in captivity for a prolonged period. The one advantage in releasing adults is that, if they do survive, breeding in the wild is likely to begin sooner than is the case when young birds are released. This is particularly true with larger species such as the vultures where birds often make their first breeding attempt when up to five or six years old. The Griffon Vulture project in southern France involved the release of some captive-reared adult birds and resulted in successful breeding in the wild only two years after the first birds were released.

Cross-fostering, where the young or eggs from one species are placed in the nest of another, has been used with Peregrines and Lesser Kestrels. In the case of the Peregrine in Germany, some of the young birds were placed in wild Goshawk nests in an attempt to re-establish a tree-nesting population of Peregrines. Although there may be concerns that a bird's behaviour could be altered if it is reared by adults of a separate species, there has been some initial success using this technique.

Some people have reservations about using reintroduction in order to restore lost species, seeing such projects as unnatural human interference. One birding magazine in Britain has gone as far as using the prefix 'real' when referring to Red Kites in Wales as if to suggest that the reintroduced birds are less worthy of attention. Whilst it is easy to understand that seeing a Kite with wing-tags is less satisfying for some people than watching a wild-fledged bird, untainted by the hand of man, in mid-Wales, it is important to try and take a long-term view of what may be achieved by reintroduction. More than ten years on from the start of the programme, Kites are now breeding freely again in four areas of England and Scotland. Although some of the young are still currently fitted with wing-tags as an aid to monitoring, these populations will hopefully need no further human assistance in order to continue to increase and spread out to new areas. A countryside without Kites is actually the more unnatural situation, as it is the direct result of past human interference and persecution on a huge scale. Without the reintroduction project this unnatural situation would have persisted for decades and many people would have been deprived of the opportunity of watching such a spectacular species in their local countryside.

Table 6: Bird of prey reintroduction projects in Europe
(see Cade (2000) for a full review of reintroduction projects involving diurnal birds of prey worldwide)

SPECIES	AREA	DATES	REINTRODUCTION METHODS	PROGRESS	ORGANISATIONS INVOLVED	COMMENTS
White-tailed Eagle	Western Scotland	1959-1998	Nestlings taken from Norway and hacked from release site	131 birds released 1975-1997; first successful breeding 1985; 19 pairs reared 12 young in 2000	Scottish Natural Heritage and RSPB	Unofficial releases in early stages unsuccessful. Coordinated programme began 1975
Golden Eagle	Donegal, Republic of Ireland	Proposed 2001	Nestlings to be collected from Scotland and hacked from release site		Irish Raptor Study Groups	
Goshawk	Britain	1960s-ongoing	Birds imported from northern and central Europe for falconry escaped or deliberately released	Estimated 250+ birds released/escaped; c. 350 pairs by late 1990s	Mainly individual falconers	Lack of organised release programme with monitoring so relative importance of natural recolonisation and releases not known
Buzzard	Norfolk and Sussex, England	1994-ongoing	Hacking wild-taken nestlings from artificial nest sites	Over 40 birds released by 1997; dispersal and survival rates similar to wild populations; several breeding pairs established, involving at least one released bird	Institute of Terrestrial Ecology (now Centre for Ecology and Hydrology)	An experimental project to study dispersal and survival in low density populations
Osprey	Rutland Water, central England	1996-ongoing	Nestlings taken from Scotland and hacked from release site	52 birds released by 2000; several birds returned to release area from wintering grounds	Leicestershire and Rutland Wildlife Trust, Anglian Water and Highland Foundation for Wildlife	Too early to assess results but early signs encouraging
Griffon Vulture	Cévennes, southern France	1980-86	Captive-reared adults and immatures hacked from release site	61 birds released; first breeding in 1982; colony of c.180 birds by 1995	Fonds d'Intervention pour les Rapaces	Unusual project as releases involved mainly adults. Food provisioning close to established colony

Table 6 (continued): **Bird of prey reintroduction projects in Europe**
(see Cade (2000) for a full review of reintroduction projects involving diurnal birds of prey worldwide)

SPECIES	AREA	DATES	REINTRODUCTION METHODS	PROGRESS	ORGANISATIONS INVOLVED	COMMENTS
Black Vulture	Cévennes, southern France	Started 1992	Mixture of captive-bred young and some older birds; also wild young taken from Spain. Release by hacking	20 birds released during first four years of project; successful breeding by released birds at age of 4 years; 4 pairs in 1998	Black Vulture Conservation Foundation; Fonds d'Intervention pour les Rapaces	Same release area as Griffon Vulture project – see above
Griffon Vulture	Central Apennines, Italy	Started 1994	Release of rehabilitated adults and immatures from Spain	30 birds released by 1996; high survival rates and low levels of dispersal	Natural Forest Service	Unusual project as releases involved mainly rehabilitated birds
Bearded Vulture	Alps; several countries involved	1986-ongoing	Captive-bred young hacked from release sites	Over 80 birds released; high survival rates, low dispersal; first breeding attempt 1997	Collaborative project involving WWF, IUCN and many captive breeding facilities	
Peregrine	Germany (similar work in northwest Poland)	1977-ongoing	Captive-bred young hacked from release sites, including artificial nests. Some birds cross-fostered into wild Goshawk nests	Over 800 birds released; at least 70 territorial pairs re-established by 1998	Private initiative by Deutscher Falkenorden with support from government agencies.	Many different release sites in both urban and rural areas
Peregrine	Sweden and southeast Norway	1982-ongoing	Captive-bred young hacked or fostered into wild Peregrine nests	Over 400 birds released; 48 pairs in 1997 and population increasing	Swedish Society of Nature Conservation, Swedish Environment Protection Board and others	
Lesser Kestrel	Catalonia, Spain	Started 1989	Mainly captive-bred young, either hacked or cross-fostered into Common Kestrel nests	More than 700 birds released; over 70% survived first year; first breeding in 1990, c.30 pairs by 1998	Sevei de Protecció i Gestió de la Fauna, Direcció General del Medi Natural	Some problems with secondary poisoning and predation but now resolved

There are indications that publicity resulting from the reintroduction programme has encouraged others to consider reintroductions of the same species in other parts of Britain. Several bird of prey centres hold captive Kites and some have expressed an interest in breeding from captive pairs and releasing the offspring. If these projects are to go ahead, it is vital that they are well planned and have the resources necessary for adequate monitoring of released birds. There have already been well-publicised problems with inappropriate releases of captive-bred Barn Owls. These have included releases into areas with unsuitable habitat, where the birds have little chance of survival, and releases into areas where wild Barn Owls are still present, risking the spread of disease and increasing the level of competition for food. In Britain, projects involving Barn Owls must now meet strict guidelines and require a licence from the Department of the Environment, Transport and the Regions.

juvenile

adult

Black Kite

adult

juvenile

juvenile

juvenile

adult

DAN POWELL

Adult and juvenile Kites are readily separable in the field if they are seen at close range (see text)

1. *Adult Red Kite*   *(Chris Gomersall)*

2. *Juvenile Red Kite. The extensively pale-fringed wing-coverts show that this is a first-year bird*   *(Chris Gomersall)*

3. *Black Kite. The less deeply forked tail, lack of any warm brown tones and darker appearance clearly separates the Black Kite from its closest relative*   *(Dick Forsman)*

4. *Juvenile Red Kite. The pale line formed by the tips of the wing-coverts is visible on the folded wing*   *(Mike Lane)*

5. *Twelve week old Kites just before release* *(Ian Carter)*

6. *Young Kite flying from the release aviary in central England* *(Ian Carter)*

Chapter 6

DIET AND FEEDING BEHAVIOUR

The Red Kite is a supreme generalist and opportunist scavenger, taking advantage of whatever food sources are locally available and accessible. As a result, it has been able to exploit a wide range of habitats, from the grimy streets of medieval London to the rain-soaked hills of central Wales and the hot, dry, Iberian plains – in each area depending on a very different diet.

Some live prey is taken, particularly during the breeding season, but the Kite is not powerful or aggressive, and is certainly no threat to livestock or gamebirds. As an opportunist scavenger, however, it is often the first bird on the scene when an animal dies and it is easy to see how, with its large wing-span, hooked beak and sharp claws, it acquired an unfair reputation with farmers and gamekeepers of the past.

Food spectrum

With the possible exception of its close relative the Black Kite, the Red Kite is unrivalled by any other European bird of prey in its ability to exploit such a wide variety of different prey. Here is a bird that can be seen snatching crane-flies from the air and delicately transferring them from foot to bill in a manner more befitting a Hobby, but can also be found in the company of vultures in southern Spain, feasting on the carcasses of dead cattle. Detailed studies of diet in various parts of its range have shown that the Kite will feed on almost any type of animal carrion that it comes across and a full list of species recorded would extend to many pages. Birds and mammals form the bulk of the diet in most areas but invertebrates, fish, reptiles and amphibians are all taken when available. Lord Lilford (1883) was quick to recognise the Kite's scavenging tendencies and also knew that it was, in no sense, a fussy eater:

> *Literally nothing that any bird will eat comes amiss to the Kite; and from my acquaintance with him in captivity, I am inclined to think that he prefers his food somewhat high. I have seen a Kite devour rotten cabbage-stalks, scraps of bread, potatoes, fish, flesh, and fowl, fresh, high and putrid, and complacently swallow pieces of stiff leather.*

Live prey is limited to invertebrates and other creatures small or weak enough to be overpowered by a bird not noted for its strength. Small mammals, up to the size of half-grown Rabbits are sometimes taken, as are small and medium-sized birds, particularly nestlings or recently fledged and inexperienced young.

The amount of food required each day varies, depending on such factors as temperature, stage of moult and the amount of energy expended during routine daily activities. As a rough estimate, Brown (1970) thought that a bird like the Kite, weighing about 1kg, would need 130-140g each day simply to maintain itself, the approximate equivalent of a single young Rabbit. Birds in captivity, where food intake is easy to measure, will usually consume rather less than a wild bird due to their lack of energy expenditure during the day. However, a Kite trained to fly at the National Bird of Prey Centre in Newent, Gloucestershire consumed 4-6 one-day-old chicks each day, and, at 25-30g each, this equates well with Brown's estimate (Walters Davis & Davis 1973).

Foraging techniques

In order to exploit such a wide variety of both live prey and carrion, a range of different foraging behaviours are employed. Active hunting is rarely witnessed but other types of behaviour are readily observed, and help to make the Kite such an obvious and familiar species. Flight associated with foraging differs markedly from the type of flight seen when a bird is travelling directly from one place to another. In such direct flights the bird usually proceeds purposefully in a straight line and, particularly if there is an adverse wind, uses deep, fluid wing-beats, with a noticeable rising and falling body movement, reminiscent of the flight of a tern.

High circling
The Kite's light frame and long wings and tail enable it to soar effortlessly for long periods by utilising the wind or rising thermals of air. Given suitable conditions, a Kite can circle up to several hundred metres with barely a single flap of its wings and thus very little expenditure of energy. High circling is therefore a very efficient method of searching for animal carcasses and allows a large area to be scanned in a relatively short space of time. Blanco (1982) found that Kites in southern Spain spent approximately 65% of their flying time each day above 20m and were often seen circling at much greater heights than this.

The Kite does not possess the keen sense of smell that birds such as the American Turkey Vulture use to detect animal carrion, and relies instead on its extremely sharp eyesight. Once potential food is located, it is approached gradually by descending in ever-tighter circles until only a few metres above the ground. There is often a great reluctance to land, perhaps because, in contrast to its aerial agility, the Kite, with its long tail and small feet, is rather ungainly and awkward on the ground and is therefore vulnerable to ground predators. Where possible, the carcass may be snatched up from the ground and carried to a safe feeding perch or, with very small carcasses, even devoured on the wing. With larger carcasses, too heavy to lift, the Kite will often land a few metres away and approach cautiously on foot before beginning to feed.

Low circling, gliding and hovering
When searching for smaller carcasses or invertebrates the Kite flies much closer to the ground and can frequently be seen gliding just a few metres above the fields with its head tilted downwards, scanning the ground below. Earthworms are a favourite food and in damp conditions, often early in the morning, several birds may gather over a suitable field, sometimes in the company of Buzzards, to take earthworms that have emerged from their burrows. Kites may drop down from 10m or more above the ground to take an earthworm only a few centimetres long, showing just how good their eyesight must be. Brief hovering flights are used occasionally to inspect a potential food item more closely before landing, and Kites will, at times, hang almost motionless into the wind, in order to scan the ground below in more detail.

Walking

Buzzards frequently walk or hop along the ground when searching for invertebrates and this technique is sometimes adopted by the Kite, perhaps mainly as a means of conserving energy when low temperatures and lack of wind make flying for prolonged periods more arduous. As when scavenging on animal carcasses, Kites feeding on invertebrates often land a few metres away from food they have located from the air and then walk up to it.

Active hunting

Low gliding and flapping flight is used in the pursuit of live prey, although observations of anything other than invertebrates being killed are uncommon. Davis and Davis (1981) reported several examples where birds up to the size of a Rook were chased and killed, with prey being taken either from the ground or in the air. The Kite is capable of rapid aerial pursuits, at least over a short distance, but most prey is taken by surprise rather than following a chase of any length. Prey is apparently mainly dispatched using the bill rather than the claws (Glutz Von Blotzheim, Bauer & Bezzel 1971).

The Kite's relative lack of strength and aggression restricts the size of animals that are taken and, as Yarrel (1857) describes, may prevent the predation of even small prey:

> *The Kite, like the Sparrow-Hawk, frequently visits the poultry-yard, but is not remarkable for its courage: Hens have been known by their vociferations and their show of resistance to protect their chicks from the threatened attack, and even to drive away the unwelcome intruder.*

Only rarely does the Kite resort to the perch and wait tactics, so favoured by birds like the Kestrel and Buzzard. These species are less well adapted for remaining in the air for long-periods, and watching for prey from a perch is an effective, low-cost hunting technique. The Kite's dependence on carrion, together with its lightweight frame and supreme aerial ability makes active foraging a far more effective strategy.

Food piracy

Anyone who has visited one of the winter feeding stations in mid-Wales will be aware that Kites come by much of their food by stealing it from other birds. When a Carrion Crow or Magpie is seen flying with a piece of meat, the waiting Kite flies from its perch and begins a rapid skua-like pursuit, making best use of its advantage of speed and agility. In trying to escape, the corvid may drop the food and the Kite then spirals down to take it, sometimes before it has even reached the ground. It must then try to avoid the attentions of corvids and other Kites, and the prize may change hands several times before it is finally consumed. By pirating food from other birds, there is less need to attend the unseemly mêlées of scavenging birds that often develop close to a source of food, where a lack of strength and aggression is a considerable disadvantage. At a carcass, where the weak-billed Kite may have difficulty in tearing pieces of flesh for itself, this feeding strategy allows it to exploit the more powerful scavengers present in order to gain a share of food that might otherwise be unavailable.

It is not only corvids that are vulnerable to having food stolen in this way. Snow and Perrins (1998) noted Grey Heron, Buzzard, Osprey, Goshawk, Peregrine, Hobby and White-tailed Eagle as victims of the Kite and Wildman, O'Toole and Summers (1998) added Kestrel and Sparrowhawk to the list from their observations in northern Scotland. The Kestrel was robbed of a Common Rat when on the ground, whilst the Sparrowhawk was robbed in flight of a Blackbird, presumably requiring a considerable turn of speed in order to get the better of such an able flier. Gómez-Tejedor (1998) studied foraging by scavengers at a rubbish dump in Badajoz, Spain, and recorded incidents of Kites attempting to steal food from Cattle Egrets, White Storks and Lesser Black-backed Gulls. In some cases, food may be obtained from other species without the need to steal it directly and as long ago as 1939, Uttendörfer recorded Kites scavenging on prey remains at a Peregrine nest. The aggressive way in which most intruders into a Peregrine's territory are dealt with is probably the main reason why this type of behaviour has not been recorded more frequently.

Methods of studying diet

Diet is usually determined in birds of prey by a combination of analysis of regurgitated pellets, examining food remains found at roost or nest sites, and direct observation of foraging birds. Each method provides slightly different information and each has its own inherent biases.

Pellets are relatively easy to find at communal winter roosts and at nest sites where they are produced by both the adults and well-grown nestlings. They contain indigestible material such as fur, feathers and fragments of bone from which prey can be identified, sometimes requiring the use of a high-powered microscope. Potential biases arise from differences in the amount of material that is ingested when different prey types are consumed and from variation in the durability of remains. Fur, for example, tends to survive better than feathers in the acidic stomach of raptors and so the importance of birds in the diet may be underestimated. Unlike the case with many species of owl, where prey is usually swallowed whole, it is impossible to judge from remains found in Kite pellets the relative amounts of food eaten.

Examining the remains of food at roost or nest sites provides useful information on the size as well as species of prey taken, but is biased towards larger prey where the remains are more obvious and therefore more likely to be found. Small prey such as invertebrates, small mammals and birds may be swallowed whole, leaving no remains to be found as evidence.

Direct observation of foraging birds is the only means of determining *how* food is obtained. It can reveal the extent to which prey is actively hunted rather than taken as carrion, and provides information on the importance of invertebrates such as earthworms, the remains of which do not always show up in pellets and are unlikely to be found at nest sites. This method is also likely to underestimate the importance of small prey as these may be picked up and carried to a secluded feeding perch or quickly swallowed whole making observation less likely.

Pellets regurgitated at communal roosts and nest sites provide valuable information on diet (Ian Carter)

Breeding season diet

In Table 7 each food-type is ranked as of low, medium or high importance in the diet on the basis of the information available. Whilst this, at times, required a rather subjective judgement, it at least gives an indication of relative importance and allows comparisons to be made between four different areas within the Kite's range. In most cases food-types are grouped into categories, as a full list of prey species would extend to many pages for each of the different areas. Most of the information in Table 7 is derived from studies of food remains and analysis of pellets, methods which do not reveal whether prey has been taken as carrion or was killed. It can be safely assumed that the large mammals and most or all of the large birds were scavenged, as these species are too large for a Kite to kill and carry back to the nest. The breeding season is defined here as the period from nest-building through to independence of the young and varies slightly between the different areas.

The task of rearing young imposes certain restrictions on the type of prey taken, as food items for nestlings and, before the eggs have hatched, for the incubating female, must be carried to the nest site. Invertebrates are generally too small to be worthwhile for this purpose and, at the other end of the scale, many animal carcasses are too heavy to be lifted. These food sources are still useful for the adults but, for the growing brood, prey of intermediate size is at a premium. Hille (1995b) carried out a detailed study of a single pair of Kites in the Rhön Biosphere Reserve in Germany and found that invertebrates, particularly earthworms and beetles, were important foods for the adults early in the season. During March and April, when wet weather was frequent, the pair spent much time foraging on the ground for invertebrates. Later in the season, when the adults had young to feed, they spent more time searching for food on the wing and birds and mammals became much more important in the diet.

Small and medium-sized mammals and birds dominate the diet in Wales and England, and are also the most important groups in southern Spain. The Rabbit is the single most numerous species in the diet in these three areas and is also important in northern Scotland (Wildman, O'Toole & Summers 1998) and, to a lesser extent, in southern Sweden (Kjellén 1996). The reduction in Rabbit numbers in the 1950s following the outbreak of myxomatosis is thought to have temporarily reduced breeding productivity in mid-Wales (Lovegrove, Elliot & Smith 1990), at least until Kites had learnt to exploit alternative sources of food. In parts of Germany the Common Hamster dominates the diet, although it has declined in importance as farming methods have become more intensive and Hamster populations have crashed. This species is an ideal prey in the breeding season as, at about 300-500g, it is the equivalent of 10-15 voles or mice but is still not too heavy to be carried back to the nest. The same applies to the similar-sized Common Rat, which is frequently taken by Kites in England and Scotland. Field Voles are the most important small mammal in Wales and improved breeding success has been linked to years with high vole populations (Davis & Newton 1981). In southern Spain, Kites take significant amounts of reptiles and freshwater fish, each forming approximately 10% of the diet (Veiga & Hiraldo 1990). In southern Sweden, where birds are the most important group, 8% of the breeding season diet is made up of fish (Kjellén 1996).

Table 7: **Breeding season diet in Wales, central England, Germany (several different areas) and the Doñana National Park in southern Spain**

Information from Davis & Davis (1981), Carter & Clarke (in prep), Veiga & Hiraldo (1990), Delibes & García (1984), Ortlieb (1989), Hille (1995b) and Tony Cross (pers comm.)

Food Type	Relative importance in diet			
	Wales	**Central England**	**Southern Spain**	**Germany**
Large mammals	High: dominated by sheep carrion, including docked tails, scrota and placenta; some brought in as nest decoration rather than food	Low: sheep and deer, including Muntjac	Medium: both domestic and wild mammals	Low: including domestic species, Wild Boar, Badger and Roe Deer
Lagomorph (Rabbits and Hares)	High: Rabbits about 6 times more common than Hares	High: mainly Rabbits, fewer Hares	High: Rabbits and Hares both commonly taken; high proportion as juveniles	High: Hares more common in diet than Rabbits
Common Rat	Medium	High	Medium	Medium
Other small/medium mammals	High: including Field Vole, Mole and Hedgehog	High: small mammals mainly Field Voles; larger species including Mink, Stoat, Weasel, Mole, Hedgehog and Grey Squirrel	Medium: mainly rat and mouse species	High: Hamsters dominate breeding season diet in some areas; Common Voles also very important
Waterfowl	Medium: Black-headed Gull chicks taken frequently by some pairs	Low	High: large numbers of Coot; wide variety of other waterfowl including heron nestlings	Medium: variety of different species recorded
Corvids	High	High: many as nestlings or recently-fledged young	Medium: mainly Magpies	High: Carrion Crows, Jackdaws and Magpies common in diet in some areas
Pigeons	Medium	High: mainly Woodpigeon including nestlings	Low	High: mainly Domestic Pigeons, also Woodpigeons

Table 7 (continued): Breeding season diet in Wales, central England, Germany (several different areas) and the Doñana National Park in southern Spain

Information from Davis & Davis (1981), Carter & Clarke (in prep), Veiga & Hiraldo (1990), Delibes & García (1984), Ortlieb (1989), Hille (1995b) and Tony Cross (pers comm.)

Food Type	Relative importance in diet			
	Wales	Central England	Southern Spain	Germany
Gamebirds	Low	High: mainly full-grown Pheasants	Low	Medium: Grey Partridge most commonly recorded gamebird; fewer Pheasants
Other small/medium birds	Medium: low numbers of a wide variety of species	Medium: low numbers of a wide variety of species	Medium: low numbers of a wide variety of species	High: Domestic Fowl common in some areas; low numbers of a wide variety of other species
Small birds	Medium: low numbers of a wide variety of species	Low: small numbers of a wide variety of species	Medium: low numbers of a wide variety of species	High: mainly low numbers of a wide variety of species but Skylark and Starling more common
Amphibians/reptiles	Medium: Common Frog taken in small numbers	Low	High: lizards and snakes commonly taken, frogs less frequently	Low: lizards, snakes, frogs and toads all taken very infrequently
Fish	Low: remains from Brown Trout and Tench found at nest sites	Low: freshwater fish, presumably taken as carrion	High: freshwater fish common; marine fish also taken	Medium: freshwater fish recorded regularly in some areas, very unusual in others
Invertebrates	High: mainly earthworms and beetles; also other groups some of which probably ingested incidentally when feeding on larger prey	Medium: remains of earthworms found in pellets from nest sites	Medium: commonly taken but making up only a small proportion of diet in terms of biomass	Medium: one study of a single pair showed that earthworms and beetles were important early in the season
Human waste	High: from slaughter houses, refuse tips and feeding stations	Low	Medium	Medium: Domestic Fowl and large mammals probably scavenged from waste dumps

Wales is the only place where carrion from large mammals is important during the breeding season. Davis and Davis (1981) found evidence of sheep in no less that 75% of pellets collected during the period from April to August. The proportion was highest in spring when remains included the small red rubber rings used to dock lambs' tails and scrota. Field observations showed that sheep's placentas were also eaten. In contrast to more productive lowland areas, Welsh Kites must rely heavily on sheep carrion, waste from slaughterhouses and, more recently, feeding stations, because there are limited alternative foods available.

Adults carrying food to nest sites often do so in as inconspicuous a manner as possible, flying low down and with the talons tucked close in to the body, making small items of food very difficult to see. Viñuela (1992) has suggested that this may be in order to minimise the risk of the food being seen and then stolen by other birds of prey, including other Red Kites in the area.

Diet in the non-breeding season

Freed from the duties of provisioning young, Kites are able to exploit a far wider range of food-types outside the breeding season. Invertebrates are taken more frequently, and in Britain, earthworms are a particularly favoured food. Insects of several groups are taken frequently in some areas during the non-breeding season, including southern Spain, although they are thought to form only a very small proportion of the diet in terms of biomass.

Carrion from large mammals becomes more important in Spain and Sweden where Kites are also attracted to rubbish dumps to scavenge (Kjellén 1996). Sheep carrion continues to be important in Wales and meat provided at feeding stations supports large numbers of Kites through the cold winter months. Counts of more than 80 birds have been made at sites in Wales where food is provided each day during the winter. In central England, rubbish dumps are rarely visited and carrion from large mammals is not an important source of food. Livestock rearing in this, largely arable, area is limited and standards of husbandry are high so that few carcasses become available. There is also an abundance of carrion from smaller species that provide a more readily accessible source of food.

In Germany, Ortlieb (1989) reported that birds overwintering in Baden-Württemburg fed almost exclusively on Common Voles and only very low numbers of other mammals, birds and invertebrates were recorded in the diet. In other parts of Germany, however, refuse tips are thought to provide an important source of food. On the northern plateau of central Spain, Common Voles can form up to 80% of the diet in vole plague years (Viñuela 1994) but livestock carrion is also important, particularly in years when vole numbers are low.

Table 8: Non-breeding season[1] diet in Wales, central England and the Doñana National Park in southern Spain

Information from Davis & Davis (1981), Carter & Clarke (in prep), Heredia, Alonso & Hiraldo (1991), Blanco, Gonzalez & Hiraldo (1990), Blanco, Hiraldo & Heredia (1990)

Food Type	Relative importance in diet		
	Wales	Central England	Southern Spain
Large mammals	High: dominated by sheep carrion occasionally other wild and domestic animals	Low: sheep and deer species	Medium: both domestic and wild mammals
Lagomorph (Rabbits and Hares)	High: Rabbits much more common than Hares	High: mainly Rabbits, fewer Hares	High: Rabbits and Hares both commonly taken
Common Rat	Medium	High	High
Other small/medium mammals	High: including Field Vole, Mole and shrews	High: small mammals mainly Field Voles and Woodmice; larger species, including Weasel and Mole, less common	Medium: voles common in the diet in parts of Spain but less important in the south
Waterfowl	Low	Low	High: goose carrion very important; also ducks, rails and waders
Corvids	Medium: including Jackdaw, Magpie, Carrion Crow, Rook and Jay	Medium	Medium
Gamebirds	Low	High: mainly Pheasant, also Red-legged Partridge	Low
Other small/medium birds	High: low numbers of a wide variety of species	Medium: low numbers of a wide variety of species	High: wide variety of species
Amphibians/reptiles	Low: Common Frog taken very infrequently	Not recorded	Low
Fish	Low	Low: freshwater fish presumably taken as carrion	Low
Invertebrates	High: earthworms and beetles common in diet; wide range of other groups some of which probably ingested incidentally when feeding on larger prey	High: earthworms commonly taken; flying insects such as craneflies taken on the wing in late summer	Medium: including ants, grasshoppers and beetles; common in diet but making up only a small proportion of food in terms of biomass
Human waste	High: from slaughter houses, refuse tips and feeding stations	Low: Kites only very occasionally seen at refuse tips	Low: but waste from livestock processing factories and refuse tips important in other parts of Spain

[1] Loosely defined as August to March

81

Feeding at large carcasses

The Kite's lack of strength and relatively weak bill are a considerable disadvantage when it comes to tackling the carcasses of larger mammals, as it is necessary to penetrate the tough outer skin in order to reach the meat beneath. In Wales, it is thought that sheep meat only becomes available to Kites once more powerful scavengers such as Foxes or Ravens have broken into the carcass, or after a certain amount of decomposition has taken place. The same may be true with large mammals in Spain, as groups of Kites have been repeatedly observed loafing near to carcasses but not feeding. García, Viñuela and Sunyer (1998) noted this behaviour and suggested that the birds were waiting for larger scavengers to open up carcasses before they could begin to feed. An alternative explanation is that these birds were reluctant to fly down to the carcass until they were sure that it was safe to do so. Such cautious behaviour is known to occur in some African species of vulture where ground predators are a constant threat at carcasses. Large numbers of scavenging vultures may gather in trees near to a carcass before the bravest or, more likely, the hungriest, fly down and begin to feed. Once a few birds have demonstrated that the coast is clear, the rest quickly join in the feast (Snyder & Snyder 2000).

When individuals from several different species gather at a carcass, a dominance hierarchy is usually formed, determining which birds can feed first. This seems to vary greatly, depending on the situation and probably on the hunger of the birds involved, so that Kites are at times subordinate to Buzzards and Ravens but, on other occasions, can displace them from a carcass. When several Kites are present at a carcass they often feed together without undue squabbling.

Corvids, including Carrion Crows and Magpies also regularly attend carcasses and, whilst they are subordinate to Kites, they can cause them no little irritation in their attempts to gain a share of the food. Magpies have even been watched apparently working as a team, with one bird hopping up behind the Kite and tugging at its tail feathers, while others take advantage of the distraction in order to steal food.

The importance of live prey versus carrion

It is often suggested that Kites rely heavily on carrion during the winter but take mostly live prey in the breeding season (Davis & Davis 1981; Cramp & Simmons 1980), although there is usually not much evidence given to support this claim. Young, and therefore inexperienced, birds and mammals are available mainly in the summer and when remains are found in pellets or at nest sites it is perhaps simply assumed that they are usually killed rather than taken as carrion.

It is undoubtedly true that live prey is sometimes taken. In Wales, Walters

Davies and Davis (1973) found that some Kites visited Black-headed Gull colonies in order to take nestlings and, in one case, several rings that had been placed on gull chicks were found in pellets at a Kite nest 4km away. Steve Parr (reported by Lovegrove 1990) has seen Kites quartering low over woodland in what he interpreted as a systematic search for Crow or Woodpigeon nestlings. In England and Scotland, the partly-grown blood feathers from nestling or recently fledged corvids and Woodpigeons are frequently found at nest sites. Some of the Woodpigeon remains have involved nestlings of pre-fledging age that presumably could have only been obtained direct from nests (Carter & Clarke in prep). Taking such defenceless and immobile prey as nestlings is, in many ways, in keeping with a mainly scavenging lifestyle even though, in this case, the birds are killed.

During many hundreds of hours of direct observations in central England, aided by radio-tracking, only a single example of active hunting for prey (other than for invertebrates) has been witnessed. This involved a Kite flying low over the ground and then dropping, with talons outstretched, into long grass, probably in an attempt to catch a small mammal. In Wales, Davis and Davis (1981) recorded such behaviour in every month from June to December and reported several examples of successful attacks on full-grown birds up to the size of a Rook. Active hunting has also been regularly observed in northern Scotland (Wildman, O'Toole & Summers 1998).

It seems likely that carrion is the preferred source of food and, where readily available, in a form suitable for carrying back to the nest, it makes up the bulk of the diet in the breeding season as well as in winter. In areas where carrion is in short supply, or where a pair learns to exploit a source of easily caught live prey, active hunting may become more important.

Remains of nestlings or recently fledged young of birds such as Woodpigeon (right), Carrion Crow and Black-headed Gull are regularly found at Kite nests in Britain (Ian Carter)

Prey specialisation

Studies of food remains or pellets found at nest sites usually reveal a highly varied diet, as indicated in the tables above. At some nests, however, the remains are dominated by a particular food-type, upon which the pair has clearly learnt to specialise. Walters Davies and Davis (1973) found nests where the food remains consisted mainly of Black-headed Gulls, Magpies or Jackdaws, in each case with relatively few other species present. Hen Pheasants dominated the food remains at one nest in central England, situated only 1km away from a Pheasant laying pen, and the local gamekeeper reported that the adult Kites were frequently seen removing dead birds from within the pen. At a nearby nest, with a high proportion of surrounding woodland, 71% of pellets contained the remains of pigeon, and food remains found below the nest suggested that this pair were specialising on Woodpigeons (Carter & Clarke in prep).

Walters Davies and Davis (1973) suggested that food specialisation might continue outside the breeding season as the proportions of different food-types varied greatly in collections of winter pellets from different communal roosts within the same area. They also believed that certain individual Kites frequently foraged for invertebrates at favoured locations whilst others in the same area, and with the same opportunities, seldom did so.

Chapter 7

HABITAT AND LAND-USE

Climate and relief

Whilst the Kite does not have specific requirements for particular landscape types or climatic conditions, it does have certain preferences, and these are reflected in its pattern of distribution. As a general rule, extremes of climate are not favoured and so areas with either excessively hot and dry, or, cool and damp, conditions are often avoided. Currently, Kites breed no further north in Europe than Denmark and southern Sweden, and there is a clear tendency to avoid the damper conditions on the north-western fringe of Europe (see map, page 28). The species is, for example, absent from north-western parts of Spain and France, where a damp Atlantic climate prevails (Viñuela 1994), and, in similar conditions in central Wales, the small remnant population suffers from poor breeding productivity and has been slow to recover from past persecution. At the other end of the climatic extreme, the breeding range does not extend into the arid conditions found in North Africa and the Middle East (with the possible exception of a small remnant population in Morocco). And, within Spain, there are few Kites in the areas with the hottest and driest conditions in summer, such as the Mediterranean coast, and much of the south and east of the country (Viñuela 1994).

The reasons for avoiding these extremes of climate probably involve both direct effects on breeding productivity, through reductions in hatching success and survival rates of chicks, and indirect effects on food availability. Cool and damp conditions may reduce hatching success and certainly increase mortality rates of small chicks while they are still covered in down. It is also possible that very hot conditions have an adverse effect on Red Kite chicks although the similar Black Kite breeds successfully in areas with very hot summers. The indirect effect of poor weather on food availability is thought to be one of the reasons for the low productivity of Kites in Wales. Cool, wet weather also restricts the ability of the adults to forage for food, thus compounding the effects of lower prey densities. Newton, Davis and Moss (1981) found that, at higher altitudes in mid-Wales, egg-laying was slightly later, on average, and the proportion of nests that produced young was less than on lower ground. As well as influencing general patterns of distribution, climatic conditions also result in local, seasonal movements. Many pairs breeding in upland areas, for example, move onto lower ground in winter to escape the harsh weather found more frequently at higher altitudes.

The Kite does not commonly breed above 1,000m in southern Europe and, further north, is very uncommon at altitudes greater than 600m (Snow & Perrins 1998; Viñuela 1994). The avoidance of the more mountainous areas is no doubt strongly linked to the climatic factors discussed above, as a wet and cool climate is more likely at higher altitudes. On a more local scale, Kites tend to select areas with undulating topography so that they can utilise the rising air currents that result from wind deflected by sloping ground. Flat areas are not entirely unsuitable as lift for foraging flights can be derived from thermals in sunny weather but, in many areas, a distinct preference for foothills and the lower mountain slopes is apparent and flat, open plains are used less frequently. It has been suggested that, in Spain, this preference might be the result of a partial ecological segregation between the Red and Black Kite, two species with a considerable overlap in diet (Heredia, Alonso & Hiraldo 1991; Viñuela, Martí & Ruiz 1999). Black Kites are often abundant on lower ground but become less frequent in the foothills where the climate is cooler, and this perhaps allows these areas to support higher densities of Red Kites. This theory is given credence by the fact that, although some lowland areas with abundant Black Kites support few Red Kites in summer, they become important for the species in winter, when there is no competition from the migratory Black Kite.

In Britain, the Kite is currently present in only tiny fragments of its potential range but is expected to spread to new areas as the Welsh and reintroduced populations continue to expand. Even in the cool, damp, upland areas of central Wales, the species has managed to survive and increase slowly although it is clear that these conditions are far from ideal. Elsewhere in Britain, the only areas likely to be unsuitable for Kites are the highest parts of the Pennines, Cumbrian mountains and Highlands of Scotland, and the largely treeless flatlands of the East Anglian fens. Even these areas might be capable of supporting low densities of birds and, in the uplands, all but the highest ground may be utilised in summer by foraging birds.

The influence of land management

The Kite, as with many other predominantly open-country birds, has benefited greatly from the mixed landscape created by humans, and it would not have been a common bird when Europe was mainly covered in natural forest. Although the majority of foraging is carried out over open countryside, where the Kite can make best use of its superb eyesight to detect potential sources of food, woodland is also an important component of the landscape. Patches of woodland not only provide sites for roosting and nesting, but are also utilised by many of the species most frequent in the Kite's diet. In Britain, the Rabbit is the most important species in the diet throughout the year and is often most numerous on the boundaries between woodland and open fields. Woodpigeons, Pheasants and corvids are also frequent in the diet and all require woodland for nesting, roosting and shelter.

With the possible exception of its close relative, the Black Kite, the Red Kite is probably more closely associated with human activities in the countryside than any other bird of prey in Europe. The bird's comparative lack of fear of man allows it to take advantage of feeding opportunities created as farming operations are carried out, and also means that food sources close to human habitation are not ignored. As a result, the Kite is a species with which local people often become familiar in the areas where it occurs.

Arable farmland

Landscapes dominated by intensively managed arable farmland are not ideal for Kites as the densities of most potential prey species will be relatively low on land that is cultivated on a regular basis and subject to routine pesticide treatment.

However, areas where this land-use predominates are not avoided completely, as long as there is at least some variation in the landscape. Alternative habitats are particularly important in the latter part of the breeding season when arable crops are well grown, as Kites are reluctant to land in thick vegetation and, in any case, food on the ground is difficult to detect when obscured by dense crops. Arable farmland is used much more frequently in autumn and winter and, in Spain, extensive, virtually treeless, expanses of arable farmland support large numbers of wintering Kites (García, Viñuela & Sunyer 1998).

In central England, observations of birds in autumn and winter showed that arable fields were utilised in roughly the same proportion as they were present in the study area (Table 9). The same pattern was apparent when only observations of feeding birds were included, showing that arable fields do provide perfectly suitable foraging habitat at this time of year (Carter & Clarke in prep).

Table 9: **Land-use categories utilised by Kites in central England, September-February, 1995-99 (Carter & Grice 2000)**

Land-use	% Red Kite observations	% each land-use class in the study area
Arable farmland	62	60
Grassland	26	20
Woodland	11	15
Other (including built land and water)	1	5

(Based on 411 individual observations)

In eastern Germany, an increase in intensive arable farming has been blamed for local declines in breeding Kite populations and a lowering of productivity in areas supporting high population densities (George 1995). In such areas there has been a decline in grassland and alfalfa, managed for the production of livestock fodder, and a shift to the cultivation of maize, following the reunification of Germany and the subsequent influence of the European Union's Common Agricultural Policy. These areas are still capable of supporting a reasonable density of Kites but not the very high densities that were present when farmland was managed less intensively and food was more abundant throughout the breeding season.

As a result of the current overproduction of many arable crops, and the huge burden of agricultural subsidies on European Union budgets, there is increasing pressure for a switch to more environmentally friendly methods of farming. This has already led to a more varied landscape in predominantly arable areas with the introduction of statutory set-aside, where fields are left uncultivated for a year or more, and schemes such as Countryside Stewardship and Environmentally Sensitive Areas, where payments are available for a range of measures aimed at encouraging wildlife. A popular option is to leave 5m margins around the edges of cultivated fields, where pesticides and herbicides are not used. These strips support more weedy plants than the main crop, which, in turn, attracts invertebrates and provides a food source for a variety of birds and mammals. Uncultivated margins also provide greater opportunities for nesting birds, many of which would struggle to survive within the cultivated crop. As the Kite has such a varied diet, measures that increase the overall diversity and abundance of wildlife in cultivated areas, are likely to be of considerable benefit.

Livestock farming and feeding stations

Farmland managed primarily for livestock is one of the most important habitats for Red Kites throughout the year. In regions where livestock is reared extensively, being left to roam over large areas of relatively poor quality grazing, the animals themselves become an important source of food. This has long been the case in central Wales where sheep grazing is the major land-use. Sheep carrion is taken by Kites throughout the year but is particularly important in late winter, when the mortality of adult ewes reaches a peak, and in spring during the lambing season. Davis and Davis (1981) refer to the period between late autumn and early spring as the 'hungry gap' when other sources of food are scarce in the unproductive landscape of mid-Wales. Sheep carrion helps to bridge this gap, providing a valuable source of food that, as a result of increased sheep mortality, is more abundant when weather conditions are at their worst and extra food is most needed.

Over the last few decades, large areas of the Welsh uplands have been fenced off and are now managed as improved pasture. These areas still provide some sheep carrion in winter, and at lambing time, and they are also much used by Kites hunting for invertebrates, particularly earthworms during wet weather. They are seen as visually intrusive by some, as the fields replace semi-natural areas of moorland and the bright green, artificial, swards stand out sharply in the landscape. However, because of the relative abundance of invertebrates in these heavily manured pastures and the resulting increases in Starlings, Moles and corvids, for example, they have probably been an overall benefit to the Kite (Lovegrove 1990).

In Spain, Viñuela (1993) found that Kites were often associated with cattle rearing areas in the breeding season, and with pig and chicken farms throughout the year. This was thought to be mainly because of the overall abundance of potential prey in these areas rather than a direct result of the presence of the livestock. In the cattle-rearing areas, for example, rodents and small birds such as Starlings were common, attracted by the high numbers of invertebrates able to thrive in the dung-enriched pastures. Livestock carrion is an additional source of food in these areas, mainly in winter when other prey species are less easy to come by.

Regions where fighting bulls are reared provide some of the best areas for breeding Kites in Spain. These areas are relatively undisturbed, as, for obvious reasons, few people are inclined to wander over the fields where the bulls are grazing. There is also usually little or no hunting activity and so levels of persecution are likely to be low. A rather more unexpected reason why cattle rearing areas may be preferred in the breeding season is the use of cattle dung as a nest building material (Viñuela 1993). It is not known why this material is favoured and, even in cattle rearing areas, not all pairs use it, so it is likely to be only a minor factor in determining local breeding densities.

The disposal of dead livestock on open dumps, referred to as 'middens' in Scotland, and, in Spain, as 'muladares' (mule dumps), provides sites where Kites can gain access to a predictable source of food in the form of animal carrion. The degree to which such sites are used depends on the availability of alternative foods but it is known that, in some areas, they can be very important, particularly in winter. A study in north-eastern Spain found that carrion from domestic animals made up between 39 and 54% of the diet for wintering birds at three different communal roosts (Larraz 1999). And García, Viñuela and Sunyer (1998) found that the proportion of chicken remains found in pellets was positively related to the density of chicken farms with 10km of communal roosts. In central and northern Europe, livestock carrion is also important for birds that remain during the winter, particularly in years when alternative prey, such as voles, is not abundant.

Abattoirs, rubbish tips and factories where livestock carcasses are processed also provide sites where waste products form a predictable food supply. In Wales, small slaughter-houses were formerly much used by Kites in winter but stricter European Union regulations governing these facilities has meant that many have long-since closed down (Davis & Davis 1981). In Spain, meat factories that process pigs, sheep and cattle often produce considerable waste such as intestines and other less valuable parts of the carcass, and are much frequented by scavengers. A refuse tip in Cantimpalos, where slaughter-house remains were common, attracted up to 300 Kites, thought to be the largest feeding concentration ever recorded (García, Viñuela & Sunyer 1998).

There has been a great deal of concern about the effects on scavenging birds of prey of tighter EU regulations relating to the disposal of animal carcasses. It is now illegal in EU countries to dump livestock carcasses in the open countryside and they must, instead, be burnt, buried or dumped at specially built, covered sites where they are generally not accessible to birds of prey. In areas where this legislation is strictly enforced, there are likely to be adverse effects on scavengers, particularly the larger vulture species in southern Europe, for which the carcasses of larger mammals form the bulk of the diet. The Bearded, Griffon, Black and Egyptian Vulture are all listed as *Species of European Conservation Concern* and, although they are now increasing following past reductions due to persecution, the decrease in the availability of carrion from large domestic animals may well be restricting rates of expansion and population densities (Tucker & Heath 1994). Kites are unlikely to be as seriously affected as the vultures, as they are less dependent on large carcasses, but there may still be local effects as this type of food becomes less easily available in future.

The deliberate provision of food for scavenging birds of prey, in ways that conform to the legislation on disposal of livestock, should go some way to compensating for the loss of carcasses in the open countryside. Feeding stations have long been used as a conservation tool for maintaining vulture populations in several southern European countries, particularly in areas where reintroduction projects have been carried out. In Wales, several feeding stations aimed primarily at Red Kites have now been established, including the centre at Gigrin Farm, set up as part of the 'Kite Country' initiative, with the aim of encouraging a greater appreciation of the Kite and its environment. At this site, pieces of meat small enough to be snatched up from the ground are put out at the same time each day, in front of specially built hides from which the spectacular display can be witnessed at close range. The meat is of a quality suitable for human consumption so that regulations on waste disposal are not infringed. Some people dislike the idea of this type of food provisioning, seeing it as unnatural and likely to change the patterns of behaviour of foraging birds by encouraging large numbers into a relatively small area. Whilst feeding sites certainly do lead to concentrations of birds, these are perhaps little different from the gatherings that have always occurred wherever animal waste from human activities has been available, including, as far back as medieval times, within our towns and cities.

On a more local scale, householders in southern England have managed to entice Kites into their village gardens by providing food on a regular basis. One such individual told a reporter from the Sunday Telegraph (17th May 1998) that he provided chicken scraps and dead mice on the back lawn and described how the Kites flew in 'like Stuka bombers' to snatch up and fly off with the food.

Agricultural operations
Village (1990) described how Kestrels took advantage of harvesting operations in order to prey on small mammals. This is an apparently regular occurrence in the Fens of eastern England where sugar-beet and potato-harvesting machinery is followed and the mammals taken as they are disturbed. Image (1992) recorded Montagu's Harriers following farm machinery in eastern England and thought that they were taking small mammals or the chicks of ground-nesting birds. Flocks of gulls following the plough are a far more familiar sight and, in this case, it is earthworms and other invertebrates that are taken as they are exposed by the action of the plough. Kites regularly feed on both small mammals and invertebrates, and there is little doubt that they too take advantage of agricultural operations.

Farmers in central England frequently see Kites when they are working in the fields, and often remark on how close the birds come to their tractor or combine harvester. Kites are also observed foraging in fields where farm operations have taken place within the past few days, including stubble fields following harvest, grass fields cut for silage, and recently ploughed fields. It is usually impossible to see what the birds are feeding on in these situations but the food items picked up are almost always very small and could well include invertebrates and small mammals killed during the farm operations. This may explain the high numbers of the normally nocturnal Woodmouse found in pellets in autumn and winter. This species is common in crop fields and many are probably killed or injured when ploughing destroys their burrows. In mid-Wales, Walters Davies and Davis (1973) reported that Kites took both invertebrates and small mammals after grass fields were cut for hay and suggested that some of the small mammals were likely to have been killed or injured during the cutting process. Kites regularly follow farm machinery in northern Scotland and have become a very familiar sight to some tractor drivers. Brian Etheridge has described two activities that are particularly attractive to foraging Kites – the spring ploughing of winter stubble and the cutting of hayfields in late summer. He has even seen 2-3 Kites swooping down to the ground behind a tractor, almost lost to view amongst a mêlée of Black-headed and Common Gulls.

Records of birds following farm machinery are frequent on the Continent. A Black and Red Kite were seen to follow a mowing machine as it cut a hayfield in the Auvergne, France, and both birds made regular stoops to the ground as if picking up food items (Warren 1989). In Germany, Ortlieb (1989) reported that Kites and Buzzards often take small mammals disturbed when arable fields are ploughed. A photograph in his book *Der Rotmilan* shows two Red Kites circling directly above a tractor as it ploughs a field, and a Buzzard standing on a recently ploughed part of the same field. In Spain, groups of up to 70 birds have been seen foraging in association with farm machinery as a field is ploughed. Viñuela (1992) thought that these birds were probably taking advantage of Common Voles, killed, or forced out into the open, as their burrows were destroyed. Hille (1995b) recorded details of foraging flights over various habitats in the Rhön Biosphere Reserve in Germany during spring and summer in 1994. She found that foraging birds were most successful in locating food when flying over meadows where farming operations (hay cut, turned or collected) had been carried out in the previous 1-2 days.

Game rearing

In parts of lowland Britain, large numbers of gamebirds (mainly Pheasants and Red-legged Partridges) are reared and released in order to provide a surplus for the shooting season. Densities are extremely high in some areas, which, in turn, can lead to high levels of mortality, and provide a valuable source of carrion for the Kite.

The management of Pheasants on shooting estates involves the use of large open-topped pens where the laying birds are housed so that their eggs may be collected and incubated artificially. The chicks are then reared indoors before being placed in release pens where food is provided and where they can gradually adapt to life in the wild. Kites have learnt that both laying pens and release pens are a likely source of dead birds and gamekeepers in England frequently see them flying low overhead or even diving down into a pen to retrieve a carcass. A Pheasant carcass would normally be too heavy for a kite to carry but those that die as a result of disease are often in poor condition and may therefore be light enough to be taken back to the nest.

On shoot days throughout the autumn and winter season, large numbers of gamebirds are killed as birds are driven by beaters over lines of guns. Most of the dead birds are picked up by gun-dogs but, inevitably, not all are retrieved and those that are missed become available to scavengers. Birds that are 'pricked' by pellets from a shotgun, but not killed outright, may die later, providing a further source of carrion. Some gamekeepers in England have reported that Kites appear in an area as soon as the shooting starts, as if they have learnt to associate the noise of gunfire with the chance of obtaining food. If these reports are anything other than coincidence then such behaviour offers a welcome contrast to the times, not so long ago, when game-rearing estates would have been very dangerous places for a Kite to search for food.

Estates where shooting is important will tend to be managed in a way that encourages gamebirds. This may include leaving field margins uncultivated, maintaining a high density of hedgerows in order to provide nest sites, and retaining areas of woodland for shelter and to provide flushing points so that Pheasants can be driven over the guns. This sort of management encourages a diversity of other wildlife, including species such as the Rabbit, Brown Hare, small mammals and birds that are often important in the Red Kite's diet. Some species also benefit from the grain feeding stations and strips of game cover crop provided by game-keepers to reduce the chance that gamebirds will stray away from the estate. Whatever the moral objections some people have to the shooting of birds for sport, there is no doubt that shooting estates offer considerable opportunities to a whole range of wildlife, including the Kite.

Pest control
Farmers and gamekeepers frequently undertake pest control programmes in order to protect gamebirds, livestock or crops, and this provides another regular food source for the Kite.

Rabbits are almost universally disliked by farmers and are controlled by trapping or night shooting with a rifle and high-powered lamp. When large numbers are shot they are frequently left where they fall, as carcasses have little value, and it is time consuming to collect them all. Sometimes they are delibera-tely left as food for Foxes in order to reduce the chance of predation of livestock or gamebirds, and some farmers now leave them specifically in order to feed the local Kites. Rabbits controlled and left out in the open in this way provide an attractive and often abundant food source.

Another regular target for pest control is the Common Rat, especially on arable farms where grain provides them with an abundant food supply. They may be trapped, shot or gassed but, particularly where large populations have built-up, poisoning is the most reliable means of control. As the usual anticoagulant rodenticides take several days to work effectively, Rats may die some distance from where the bait was eaten and, as a result, even Rats poisoned inside farm buildings can become available to scavengers if they die outside. Rats form an important part of the Kite's diet in many areas but, where poisoned Rats are taken, there is the very real risk of secondary poisoning, a subject that is covered in more detail in Chapter 11.

Other pest species regularly controlled by gamekeepers, farmers and foresters include the Stoat, Weasel, Mink, Grey Squirrel, Woodpigeon and several members of the corvid family. Trapping is the main method of control for the mammals and corvids and so carcasses only become available to Kites if the individual checking the traps leaves them out in the open. Woodpigeons, however, are often shot as they fly in to feeding or roosting areas and scavengers may take those not subsequently collected for human consumption.

Forestry
A certain amount of forest cover is an important part of a Kite-friendly landscape as it provides nesting and roosting areas, together with habitat for some of the species most important in the diet. Only relatively small patches of woodland are

required for breeding sites and communal roosts and, with the exception of clear-fells and newly planted areas, foraging is carried out over unforested open ground. It is therefore easy to see that, above a certain threshold level, forest cover may become detrimental to Kites, restricting the area available for foraging and therefore limiting the number of birds that an area is able to support.

Afforestation has long been a major concern in central Wales, as it was feared that the loss of upland sheep grazing would reduce foraging opportunities for Kites and lead to reductions in survival and breeding productivity. From the early 1960s there was a major expansion of afforestation schemes, encouraged by government incentives provided to boost timber production. As a result, more than 25% of the Welsh uplands are now under conifers, although the figure for the main area utilised by Kites is rather lower at around 16%. Research has been undertaken in central Wales specifically to find out whether this increase in forest cover has had an adverse effect on the local Kites (Newton, Davis & Moss 1996). This work showed that, despite the loss of a few breeding territories as a result of afforestation, overall, there was no noticeable negative effect on distribution or breeding productivity. In fact, in the first 12-15 years, newly planted areas with only small trees and plenty of rough grassland, support high densities of voles, an important food source for Kites. It was also suspected that increased afforestation led to a drop in incidents of illegal poisoning as this practice is carried out mainly by sheep farmers trying to protect livestock. Despite these findings, there is no doubt that mature plantations do not provide suitable foraging areas and so, above a certain level, afforestation is bound to have an adverse effect on Kites. In Wales, where the population is still recovering from past persecution, breeding densities may not yet have reached the level at which a reduction in the available foraging area has a noticeable effect.

Road-kills

This is yet another example of how the adaptable Kite is able to take advantage of a source of food that has only become available in relatively recent times, as a direct result of one of man's major impacts on the environment. It is now difficult to travel more than a few hundred metres on any busy road without seeing the evidence of birds and mammals killed by passing vehicles. Marchant and Gregory (1999) suggested that rising traffic densities and the resultant increase in road-kills could help to explain increases in the numbers of Rooks and other scavenging corvids in the United Kingdom. The Kite, being a carrion specialist, undoubtedly also benefits from this source of food.

Crows and Rooks have become adept at exploiting road casualties, taking advantage of even small gaps in the traffic on our busiest roads and motorways in order to feed. Kites are much more hesitant in such situations and are only infrequently seen scavenging on road-kills. They probably only visit the busier roads in early morning when there is little traffic and few people around. Smaller carcasses may be carried to a nearby field or tree where they can be eaten in safety but Kites will, on occasion, feed at the roadside, usually after first circling in ever tighter circles to make sure that the coast is clear. Evidence that Kites take road casualties comes not only from direct observations but also from studies of food remains. In England, bird carcasses found at nest sites sometimes have a broken wing, presumably sustained when hit by a vehicle, and some mammal carcasses retrieved from nests are squashed almost flat as a result of passing vehicles, before they were picked up from the road and carried to the nest.

Viñuela (1997) was concerned that a census of Kites in Spain carried out using road-transect counts could overestimate the population because birds were specifically attracted to roads in order to scavenge. The problem was most apparent in northern Spain where Kites were not only attracted by road-kills but also by the high numbers of voles inhabiting roadside ditches.

Many species are probably only available to Kites as road casualties, as they are unlikely to be taken as live prey and deaths from natural causes normally occur in thick cover where the carcasses are inaccessible. In Britain, examples include the Moorhen, Little Owl and Hedgehog, as all have been found as food remains at nest sites and, as a result of their behaviour, all are regular victims on our roads.

Chapter 8

THE BREEDING SEASON

In parts of Europe where the Red Kite is not migratory, many established breeding pairs stay together during the winter, spending much time close to their nest site. Some pairs, particularly those on the higher ground, where food is not always easy to come by, leave the breeding area and range more widely, perhaps taking advantage of refuse tips or a winter feeding station. Most of these pairs will have returned to their breeding sites by late February and, in Britain, most of the activity relating to territory establishment takes place during March when breeding pairs are often very conspicuous near to the nest site. By early April, most nests have been built or refurbished ready for laying. The season begins slightly later in the mainly migratory populations in central and northern Europe where most adults return to their breeding sites during March.

Age of first breeding

In areas providing ideal habitat in England and Scotland most Kites breed for the first time when they are two years old. In England this is almost always the case and birds probably only delay breeding beyond this time if, as a result of a local imbalance in the sexes, for example, they are unable to find a mate. In Scotland, most birds also begin breeding when two years old but some, mainly males, make their first attempt when in their third or even fourth year (Evans *et al* 1999). In Wales, there is a significantly greater spread in age of first breeding. Studies of wing-tagged birds have shown that many do not breed until their third or fourth year and some are not recorded breeding for the first time until they are as old as seven (Cross & Davis 1998; Newton, Davis & Davis 1989). This difference reflects the less than ideal habitat and lower food availability in mid-Wales. Kites find it more difficult to get into breeding condition and may only achieve this when they are older and more experienced.

First-year Kites sometimes pair up and hold territory, and may even construct a nest. By doing so they gain valuable experience for the following year when they have a much higher chance of success. Remarkably, reintroduced Kites in England and Scotland have occasionally bred successfully in their first year. The handful of cases where this has been recorded has mainly involved a first-year bird paired with an older bird, but, in one case in southern England, two birds in their first year bred successfully, rearing a single chick (Evans, Cordero & Parkin 1998). DNA fingerprinting was used to confirm that the two first-year birds holding territory were indeed the true parents of the chick.

By studying individually marked reintroduced birds in Britain, Evans *et al* (1999) showed that breeding productivity improved as birds became more experienced during their first 3-4 years of life. A total of 72 birds in their second year reared, on average, 1.6 young per breeding attempt, whereas 88 more experienced birds, aged three years or more, reared an average of 2.3 young per breeding attempt.

The breeding pair and site faithfulness

Kites are, in some ways, rather similar to humans in their mating strategy. Once paired, they usually remain together until the death of one of the pair, but, occasionally, 'divorces' are recorded. This is more likely to occur when an established pair fails to rear any young. If one member of the pair then has the opportunity to join up with a more successful bird then it may do so in order to improve its chances of breeding successfully in the following season. Extra-pair copulation, where a rival male mates with a paired female is also known to occur, although is probably unusual (Mougeot 2000). Studies of individually-marked birds has revealed a behaviour that is rather less frequent in humans – the pairing of very closely related individuals. This occurred in 1997-2000 in northern Scotland when a brother and sister, reared at the same nest in 1995, paired up and reared a total of seven young in four successful nesting attempts. There has also been a father-daughter pairing in the same area (Brian Etheridge pers comm.). Such incestuous pairings may be more frequent in species like the Kite where young often return to near their natal site to breed and are therefore more likely to come into contact with their parents or siblings. It is probable, although not known for sure, that individuals cannot recognise close relatives when they come across them later in life and so, despite the possible genetic disadvantages of inbreeding, a small proportion of these pairs occur purely by chance.

There have been instances where a third Kite is present in an occupied territory during the breeding season and is apparently tolerated by the resident pair (Walters Davies & Davis 1973). These birds, sometimes referred to as 'aunties', are most likely to be young reared on the territory in the previous year and are perhaps tolerated because they are closely related to the breeding pair. In northern Scotland, Brian Etheridge has reported at least two instances where young females, fledged in the previous year, were present close to the nest during the following breeding season.

Van Kleef and Bustamante (1999) recorded the first ever example of polygamous mating in the Red Kite in Doñana National Park, southern Spain in 1997. A single male, identifiable by its colour ring, helped two different females to build nests about 750m apart and was seen mating with both. Only one of the females was helped to provision the young with food but, despite this, both nests were successful in producing at least one fledgling.

Breeding pairs tend to remain faithful to a particular territory, returning year after year to breed at the same site. Pairs do sometimes move to an alternative breeding site, but this is usually within 10km, and often much closer. Once a territory has been established it will frequently remain in use for many years even if something happens to the initial pair. One such traditional site in mid-Wales was used continuously for at least 17 years, and some Welsh sites, known to be occupied over 100 years ago, are still in use today (Walters Davies & Davis 1973).

The early season

Unlike many birds of prey, including the Buzzards with which they so often share the landscape, Kites do not defend exclusive feeding territories from others of their own kind. They do, however, defend a small area around the nest site, usually extending to no more than a few hundred metres from the nest itself. First-year Kites passing near to the nest area are often ignored, probably because Kites do not normally breed until they are at least two years old and so the established breeding pair may not consider these youngsters to be a significant threat. Intruding adults, on the other hand, could be on the lookout for a breeding site or even a mate and are chased away vigorously. Mougeot (2000) found that the resident male would even attack a decoy bird, painted to look like an adult, and placed close to the nest of an established pair early in the season.

Courtship display lacks the flamboyance seen in some other birds of prey and is mainly restricted to slow circling above the nest wood involving one or both members of the pair. From just above the level of the trees, a pair may ascend to a considerable height, becoming mere specks in the sky or even disappearing into low clouds, before descending again. Sometimes a period of circling ends with a bird folding back its wings and plunging down though the canopy into the wood, usually close to the point where the nest will be built.

Another form of display commonly seen near the breeding site involves two birds flying very close together with one following closely behind the other and both using deep, exaggerated wing-beats. It is sometimes followed by a vigorous pursuit, as if one bird is trying to drive away the other, and so may be an essentially aggressive interaction between one of the resident breeding pair and an intruding bird. This display is also seen well away from the nearest breeding site, and even outside the breeding season, when it possibly involves birds trying to assess each other as potential mates. A similar type of 'butterfly' display-flight is performed by unpaired birds close to their territory, sometimes at considerable height, when it may serve as a means of attracting a potential mate.

More spectacular aerial activity, including talon-grappling and rapid, roller-coaster chases, sometimes takes place between members of a pair but also occurs during aggressive encounters between rival birds. In one extreme incident, witnessed by Peter Davis in Wales, two birds with talons interlocked spiralled downwards together and ended up crashing into the woodland canopy. Even more unfortunate were 'two males' described by Montagu (1833):

> [They were] so intent in combat, that they both fell to the ground, holding firmly by each other's talons, and actually suffered themselves to be killed by a woodman who was close by, and who demolished them both with his bill-hook.

Kites become more vocal in the breeding season and their shrill, whinnying calls, made as the pair circle together, are a familiar sound in Kite country.

The Kite's relationship with the local corvids, particularly Ravens in Wales and Carrion Crows throughout Britain, alters radically during the breeding season. These species are potential predators of eggs and small chicks but, even well before the eggs are laid, individuals flying too close to the nest site are attacked and chased with a vigour that seems strangely out of character for such a normally placid bird. The attacks rarely result in physical contact but an intruding Crow is sometimes pursued for several hundred metres before the Kite gives up and heads back to the nest area. From a human standpoint it is easy to believe that such aggression is fuelled by a desire for revenge as, for most of the year, it is the Kite which is on the receiving end of interactions between the two species. In reality, the attacks serve the useful purpose of persuading the Crows to nest elsewhere, thereby avoiding the potential for more serious conflict when there are eggs to protect.

Other birds of prey are sometimes treated in the same way and if a pair of Buzzards are holding territory in the same wood, there may be frequent bouts of aerial sparring. The two species appear to be relatively evenly matched during these aerial battles with the threat carried by the Buzzard's superior power counteracted by the greater manoeuvrability of the Kite. Perhaps, for this reason, most interactions end with neither species gaining the upper hand. Buzzards and Kites clearly learn to tolerate each other and it is not infrequent to find them nesting in close proximity in the same area of woodland. As a general rule, there is not the same level of tolerance between Kites and Carrion Crows and it is unusual to find active nests of the two species within two hundred metres or so of each other. This is not a hard and fast rule, however, and the two species have even been found nesting in the same individual tree in central Wales (Tony Cross pers comm.).

It is not unusual for a pair of Kites that are apparently settled on a territory early in the season, to suddenly switch to an alternative site, up to several kilometres away. This may be the result of disturbance at the initial site but some pairs are perhaps simply undecided as to which breeding site to use until just before the eggs are laid. Several important factors, such as the degree of human disturbance or the number of potential nest predators in an area, can only be assessed reliably by spending time on a territory and it seems that some pairs spend time at two or more sites before committing themselves to, what they consider to be, the most suitable. This behaviour is frustrating for fieldworkers as Kites are at their most active in their territories early in the season. Breeding pairs may be located relatively easily at this stage, only, in some cases, to be absent when the site is visited again later in the season.

The nest site

Although the Kite is not at all fussy about the species of tree used for nesting, there is a preference for trees large enough to provide a suitable secure fork in which to lodge the nest. In Wales, nests have been found at heights of 4-30m with the majority being between about 12 and 15m (Cross & Davis 1998). In the Chilterns of southern England, the majority of nests are over 15m high, mainly because the Beech trees so often used have few substantial branches below this height. In central and northern Spain, nest height varies considerably depending on the species of tree used. Those in Poplars are often well above 15m, whereas nests in the smaller pines tend to be much lower. In Germany, there is also considerable variation with nests found in the range 4-30m and an average height of approximately 18-20m (Ortlieb 1989).

Such a long-winged bird as the Kite requires a good aerial route to the nest and therefore generally chooses an open site with well-spaced trees, often close to the edge of a wood, or adjacent to a woodland ride or clearing. For this reason, unthinned commercial plantations, where the trees are densely packed together with few large gaps, are mostly avoided. The frequent use of Oak woods in mid-Wales (Newton, Davis & Moss 1981) and Beech woods in southern England reflects the abundance of these two woodland types in the respective areas. In central England there is a greater mix of different species and, despite an apparent overall preference for Oak, a wide variety of different tree species have already been used (Table 10). In northern Scotland a wide variety of tree species are also used, with Scots Pine the most frequently recorded, reflecting its abundance in the area (Brian Etheridge pers comm.).

Table 10: **Kite nest sites in central England, 1996-2000**

Tree species	No. nests	Nest height Average (range) in metres
Broadleaf		
Oak (English/Sessile)	18	15 (11-20)
Turkey Oak	1	20
Field Maple	1	10
Sycamore	1	15
Ash	2	18
Conifer		
Norway Spruce	3	10 (8-12)
Scots Pine	3	14 (9-17)
Larch	2	15.5 (11-20)
Total	**31**	**15 (8-20)**

Kites usually choose a substantial fork in a mature tree for their nest site, building the nest either against the main trunk or among branches within the canopy. A particularly favoured location is the point where the trunk splits into smaller branches that spread upwards into the canopy as this provides a secure fork with many supporting branches against which to rest the nest. Less often, the nest is built resting precariously on a branch some distance out from the main trunk of the tree where there is a risk of collapse in high winds. One nest in central England, built by an inexperienced first-year pair, was constructed on the flimsiest of branches about 10m high in a small spruce tree, despite an abundance of large mature Oaks nearby. Each time the incubating bird left the nest, the branch waved alarmingly up and down and this was the probable cause of subsequent breeding failure. An intact egg found on the ground below the abandoned nest had almost certainly been accidentally ejected due to the unstable position of the nest.

Nest building is normally concentrated into a few weeks (sometimes even a few days) in March and early April, just before the eggs are laid, although the odd stick may be added to a nest at almost any time from January onwards. Both the male and female help to build the nest, using sticks collected from the ground or broken from growing trees, and nest-building activity is often concentrated into the early and latter parts of the day. Observations at breeding sites suggest that it is the male that brings the majority of the material to the nest site whilst the female does most of the actual nest building.

Unpaired birds, including first-years with no intention of breeding, are often seen carrying nest material. This may be repeatedly dropped and re-caught in what seems to be no more than a game. As with other forms of play, this behaviour is probably best interpreted as practice for the time when the bird is paired up and needs to build a nest for the first time.

The nest is similar in form to that of a Carrion Crow but generally larger and more untidy, with large sticks placed in a seemingly haphazard manner to form a platform about two feet in width. The rather shallow cup, which soon becomes almost completely flat, is lined with soft, dry material such as dry grass, fur, or sheep's wool to provide a secure pad for the eggs. In Britain wool is the favoured material and is used for the lining of virtually every nest. A Kite seen flying towards a nest site with wool in its beak or trailing from its feet in early April is a good sign that the clutch will soon be laid.

Established pairs sometimes build a new nest, often using an old Grey Squirrel drey, or a Crow or Buzzard nest as a base, rather than starting from scratch. They may instead refurbish a nest used in a previous year and long-established pairs have as many as five alternatives from which to choose. Nests that are used repeatedly, with new material added each year, can become massive structures and early in the season before the surrounding trees have leaves, they are very obvious from some distance away. In southern England, 56% of successful pairs, whose composition did not change between years, reused the same nest in the following year (Evans *et al* 1999), whereas in central England, only one of 15 pairs that bred in successive years reused the same nest. The reason for such an obvious difference in behaviour between the two areas is not known, although perhaps reuse of the same nest will become more frequent in central England as population density increases.

Walters Davies and Davis (1973) found that Welsh pairs were more likely to use an alternative nest following a breeding failure in the previous year. In a study of 133 pairs, 40% of the 68 nests where the pair had failed were used in the following year, whereas the figure was 80% for the 65 nests where at least one chick fledged. The study excluded territories apparently containing only one nest where the birds had no choice of an alternative other than building a new nest. According to Brian Etheridge the same pattern is apparent in northern Scotland. Between 1992 and 2000, 65% of 85 successful pairs reused the same nest but only 11% of 18 failed pairs returned to the same nest. One of the theories put forward to explain why birds of prey have alternative nest-sites is that such behaviour is a means of avoiding parasites (Newton 1979). These may remain in a nest from one season to the next, ready to infest birds when they return in the following year. This idea does not fit well with the Welsh and Scottish data. Nests where chicks were reared successfully, and were therefore in the nest for a long period of time, are likely to support the highest parasite burdens, yet it was these nests that were most frequently used again.

The *fasciicauda* race of Red Kite (thought by some to be a hybrid between Red and Black Kite) from the Cape Verde Islands off northwest Africa has been occasionally reported using cliff-ledges or crags for nest sites (Snow & Perrins 1998), and this habit has also been recorded in Mallorca, Spain and Sicily, where the usual *milvus* race occurs (Javier Viñuela pers comm.). Nicolai (1997) mentions occasional nesting on pylons in central Europe, although such artificial situations have not been recorded in Britain.

Nest decoration

Buzzards and some other members of the Accipitridae family add fresh greenery to their nests before the eggs are laid. Kites also decorate their nests but, in keeping with their scavenging lifestyle, prefer to use rubbish, including paper, rags and scraps of plastic, for the purpose. This material can be seen hanging down from the side of an active nest or found on the ground below.

It is possible that these items are intended to form part of the nest lining but become dislodged and end up caught on sticks at the edge of the nest. It is more likely, however, that the material is used purposefully as a form of 'decoration', perhaps serving to advertise to other Kites in the area that the nest is in use. It is certainly not a new habit and Shakespeare in *The Winter's Tale* referred to it when he warned *'When the Kite builds, look to lesser linen.'* In those days, washing was sometimes left on top of a hedge to dry and the Kite was clearly not slow to take advantage. Lord Lilford, on a visit to central Spain in 1865, was told by a local that a purse containing nine dollars had once been found in a Kite's nest. And on the same trip, Lilford himself learnt of the death of President Lincoln from a scrap of Spanish newspaper found at a Kite's nest near Aranjuez (Lilford 1883).

The reintroduced birds in Britain now take advantage of more modern materials including crisp packets and supermarket bags, as well as the handkerchiefs, socks and underwear which were no doubt a mainstay of nest-decoration centuries ago and to which Shakespeare's warning referred. Oddities are sometimes found at nests, including, in recent years, a lottery ticket (unsuccessful), a plastic model dog and even the polystyrene-encased data-gathering box from a weather balloon! The two halves of the same teddy-bear were found at a nest in southern England, whilst the head of another was discovered in a nest in Yorkshire in 2000.

Orientation of nest sites

It is well known that some birds of prey tend to select nest sites facing in a particular direction more often that would be expected by chance. Watson (1997) found that Golden Eagles in Scotland preferred sites facing to the north or east rather than to the south or west and suggested that this was either to avoid exposure to inclement weather, which comes mainly from the southwest, or to avoid excessive exposure to the sun, thereby reducing the risk of the chicks overheating. Evidence from studies on Golden Eagles elsewhere in Europe suggests that the latter is the more likely explanation (Tjernberg 1983; Jordano 1981).

Newton, Davis and Moss (1981) included orientation among the factors considered when they studied the locations of Kite nests in Wales between 1946 and 1978. A considerably higher number of nests were in woods on slopes facing to the north or east than to the south or west. Northeast was the favoured direction with 29% of nests facing in this direction. In contrast, only 8%, 8% and 4% of nests were on slopes facing south, southwest and west respectively. Those involved in monitoring the reintroduced birds in southern England believe that, here too, there is a preference for nesting near to the northern or north-eastern edge of a wood (Peter Stevens pers comm.). Whatever the reasons for such preferences, Newton, Davis and Moss (1981) found no difference in breeding productivity between nests facing in different directions in Wales. If, as is likely with the Golden Eagle, sites facing to the south and west are avoided in order to reduce the risk of the chicks overheating, then the cool Welsh climate may nullify any possible disadvantage when such sites are used.

Dee Doody, who has studied Kites in Wales for many years, believes that there is another reason why woods on slopes facing northeast are preferred. He argues that access to a nest site is made easier if the adults are able to approach from downwind and, with a prevailing south-westerly wind, this is most often possible at sites sloping to the northeast. It is certainly true that when flying to perch in a tree, Kites approaching from upwind often fly directly over the tree, turn, and head back into the wind before coming to rest. It seems that it is easier for them to fly at a slow enough speed to judge the landing properly when they are flying into the wind.

Egg laying, incubation and the early chick stage

As the time for laying approaches, the female spends increasing amounts of time close to the nest and becomes much less active, relying more and more on the male to provision her with food. At this stage the breeding pair become far less obvious around the nest site. The female spends most time either on the nest or perching quietly close by, as does the male when not away hunting.

Copulations become frequent in the days before the first egg is laid, often occurring soon after the male has brought food to a perch within the nest wood. Mougeot (2000) studied 16 Kite pairs in Corsica and found that there were an average of 234 copulations for each clutch, beginning up to 40 days before the first egg was laid. By mating so frequently the male is attempting to make sure that it is his sperm that ends up fertilising the eggs and not that of a rival male who may have mated with the female while he was away searching for food. The alternative strategy of 'mate-guarding' is used by male birds of some species but is not always possible in birds of prey as the male is responsible for finding food for both himself and the female at this stage of the breeding cycle. He is therefore forced to spend time foraging away from the nest site where the female spends most of her time. Male Kites do not abandon the mate-guarding strategy altogether. Mougeot (2000) found that males at nest sites where other pairs were nesting nearby spent more time close to the nest during the pre-laying period than did males from isolated pairs. This suggests that they were well aware of the threat from rival males and kept foraging flights away from the nest to a minimum.

In Britain, most pairs lay 2-3 eggs with clutches of one or four relatively uncommon. Table 11 shows the relative frequency with which different clutches are laid in central Wales. Two eggs are far more common than three eggs, whereas in more suitable lowland habitat in England, Scotland and Continental Europe, three egg clutches are the most common (Evans *et al* 1999; Ortlieb 1989). Occasional clutches of five eggs have been recorded in central Europe (Glutz Von Blotzheim, Bauer & Bezzel 1971; Hille 1995a). Most pairs in Britain lay during the first three weeks in April with the Welsh and English birds laying, on average, slightly earlier than the Scottish birds. There is considerable variation, even between birds breeding in the same area, with some pairs already incubating by late March and others not laying until late April or even early May. Laying dates in central Europe are similar. A long-term study of Kites breeding in the Hakel Forest in eastern Germany found that the start of incubation varied from 20th March to 16th May, with a median date of 13th April. Of 858 clutches in 1958-1993, over 85% were laid sometime during the first three weeks in April (Mammen & Stubbe 1995). In southern Europe, birds in Spain begin laying in early March, well in advance of populations further north and east. The Hakel Forest study showed that the earlier laid clutches tended to produce more young than those laid later and overall breeding success was higher in the years when the majority of clutches were laid earlier than usual. This conforms to a general pattern found in many bird species and may be the result of the fittest birds being able to attain breeding condition earlier in the season (Newton 1979).

Only a single clutch is laid unless the eggs are lost early during the incubation period. If this happens then the pair may lay a replacement clutch, often in a new nest within the same territory. Late clutches in Britain, laid during late April or early May involve a combination of re-lays, following an earlier nest failure, and inexperienced first-time breeders that usually lay later than more experienced breeding pairs. Glutz Von Blotzheim, Bauer and Bezzel (1971) found that for 109 breeding attempts in Germany the mean brood size was 2.14 for first clutches and only 1.65 for replacements, the lower productivity for re-laid clutches reflecting the extra resources used up by the adult birds in producing the second clutch.

Table 11: **Clutch size in Welsh Kite nests, 1946-1996 (from Cross & Davis 1998)**

No. Eggs	No. Clutches	Percentage
1	51	6.8
2	399	53.5
3	281	37.7
4	15	2.0

Mean clutch size: 2.3 (n=746)

Kite eggs are, on average, slightly larger than a typical chicken's egg at approximately 57 x 45mm. They are usually laid on a pad of wool as at this nest in central Wales (Tony Cross)

These unhatched eggs from nests in England show the variation in shape and a typical range of markings (Ian Carter)

The female carries out the majority of incubation, either relying on food brought in by the male, or leaving the nest for short periods in order to feed, while the male takes over the nest duties. At one nest in central England, involving a pair of first-year birds, it was possible to check the sex of the incubating bird regularly by radio-tracking. On only three out of 21 checks was the male found to be on the nest. At several breeding sites in the same area, where the adults could be identified from wing-tags, the male was seen sitting on the nest on only six out of 38 visits. During poor weather, the female may not risk leaving the eggs for even a short period of time. At one Welsh nest monitored by video camera, the female remained almost motionless for a period of 36 hours during wet and windy conditions (Cross & Davis 1998), and at a nest in northern Scotland, a late, overnight, fall of snow in April covered a nest including the wings and tail of the incubating female. When Brian Etheridge visited the nest site at dawn to check on the pair, only the Kite's head with its gleaming yellow eye was visible above the blanket of white. Researchers in Wales used a light-sensitive false egg that was placed in nests in order to show for how long each day the eggs were left uncovered. Each time the egg was exposed to light, a radio-transmitter within it pulsed at a higher rate, showing that it was no longer being incubated. This work confirmed that the adults were extremely attentive and the eggs were left uncovered for only a few minutes each day (Lovegrove, Elliot & Smith 1990).

Kite eggs hatch after around 31-32 days of incubation (Snow & Perrins 1998). The incubation period has been quoted in various sources from 28 days to as much as 37-38 days. The differences stem from a combination of natural varia-tion, inaccuracy of measurements, and confusion as to how the incubation period is defined. Some authors have referred to the time taken for a single egg to hatch whilst others have given the time for the whole clutch. The female may cover the first laid eggs, in order to protect them, without actually incubating, and this period has been wrongly included in some estimates for the length of incubation. If the eggs do not hatch, as a result of infertility, or because the chicks within have failed to develop properly, the female may continue sitting for up to several weeks beyond the normal incubation period.

Once the eggs have hatched, the chicks are brooded by the female for most of the first 2-3 weeks while they are still covered with down and vulnerable to cool, damp, conditions, as well as predators. Chicks older than this may be covered in poor weather and at night, although, with a brood of three or four, this quickly becomes an impossibly difficult task. It is the male that provides the majority of the food for the chicks, particularly during the first few weeks when the female spends almost all of her time, on, or close to, the nest.

In many birds of prey and owls, eggs are laid at regular intervals and incubation begins before the final egg is laid so that the eggs hatch at intervals and there is a subsequent size difference between the chicks. In the Barn Owl, for example, the eggs hatch at intervals of 48-60 hours (Shawyer 1998) and there is a sub-stantial size difference between the oldest and youngest chicks. This is known as the 'brood reduction strategy' and it has evolved to allow birds to cope with an unpredictable food supply (Newton 1979). If there is abundant food then all the chicks get sufficient and all survive to fledging age. If there is a shortage then the largest chicks grab more than their fair share leaving the smaller ones to starve. In some species, the older chick will even attack its younger siblings when food is short, sometimes killing and eating them. Brutal though this sounds it does at least ensure that, when conditions are poor, at least some of the brood survive. If an inadequate food supply were to be shared equally then there might not be sufficient for any of the chicks to develop properly.

There has been some confusion regarding the extent to which the Red Kite adopts this strategy. It is well known that there is an interval of 1-3 days between the laying of each egg, but the time when incubation actually begins is less certain. In the late 1980s, the RSPB carried out some research in mid-Wales that involved installing video cameras at nest sites (Lovegrove, Elliot & Smith 1990). The pictures showed that the eggs usually hatched at three-day intervals, so, in this case, incubation must have started as soon as the first egg was laid. At two of the five nests monitored in this way, video pictures showed the largest chick in the nest repeatedly attacking its smaller sibling. In each case, both chicks in the nests initially grew well but, after about five days, the larger chick became aggressive each time food was brought to the nest. The smaller chick fought back at first but became progressively weaker until it eventually died (Figure 5).

Figure 5: **Feeding bouts (graphs) and number of attacks (histograms) for two nestlings monitored by video camera at a Welsh nest (from Lovegrove, Elliot & Smith 1990)**

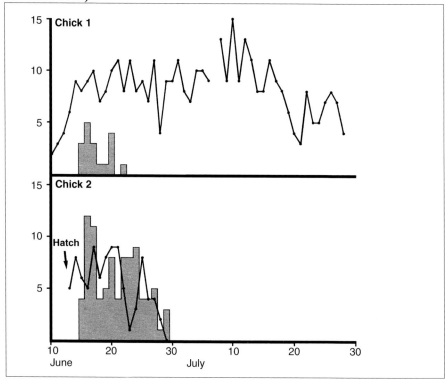

Researchers in southern Spain found a similar pattern of brood reduction, with 19 out of a sample of 37 nests losing at least one chick (attributed to starvation) before fledging (Veiga & Hiraldo 1990). This study also determined the period taken for all the eggs in a clutch to hatch and, surprisingly, found considerable variation. Most eggs from a sample of 12 two-egg clutches hatched within a single day and only one had the three day interval found in Wales. The hatching interval for three-egg clutches varied from one day to as much as 12 days (for the whole clutch to hatch) with most of the sample of nine nests somewhere in between. Clutches with the longest hatching period, and therefore the largest size difference between chicks, were more likely to suffer brood reduction due to the loss of the smallest chick. Ortlieb (1989) reported similar variation in Germany, although a gap of 2-3 days between the hatching of each egg was thought to be typical. These results show that Kites do not always begin incubation with the first laid egg and, in some cases, wait until just before the final egg is laid. It is possible that, as has been found with Kestrels (Wiebe, Korpimäki & Wiehn 1998), hatching patterns are manipulated by the adults through variations in incubation behaviour, taking into account food availability and the degree to which the food supply is predictable.

The growing brood

When the chicks are small they are fed on manageable pieces of meat by one of the adults, as, at this stage, they are unable to tear carcasses apart for themselves. As is the case with many birds of prey, this task is mainly performed by the female, although male Kites have also been recorded feeding young. At a nest site in northern Scotland, footage from a CCTV camera set up to provide live pictures to a nearby visitor centre, revealed that the male bird was particularly attentive and regularly fed the chicks, at times, even in the presence of the female.

A detailed study of a nest in central England with only a single chick showed that the male brought in almost all of the food required and the female remained close to the nest for the majority of the brood-rearing period (Medina 2000). She was therefore on hand to protect the chick from potential predators and to cover it during spells of wet weather. At nests where there are more chicks to rear, or where prey is not as abundant, the male may not be able to find all the food that is required and the female must then spend more time foraging away from the nest. In this situation there is a trade off between food provision and protection of the chicks. If both adults are away from the nest, there is a greater risk to the chicks, but, unless sufficient food is brought in, they will be unlikely to survive in any case. As the chicks grow larger they require more food but become less vulnerable to predation and so the female is more likely to leave the nest for longer periods. In exceptional circumstances, a female is capable of rearing young without any help from the male, undertaking all of the nest defence and food provisioning duties. This was recorded by Van Kleef and Bustamante (1999) in southern Spain, where a male was paired to two females but helped only one to rear young. The lone female successfully reared a single chick to fledging.

The growth rate of chicks varies to some extent, depending on the amount of food provided by the adults. When food is in short supply, the growth rate drops so that all the available resources are channelled into self-maintenance (Viñuela & Ferrer 1997). This is an important adaptation for situations where the food supply is unpredictable, as it allows the young to survive a period of food shortage before resuming more rapid growth when food becomes easier to find. The initial size difference between chicks in a nest may become exaggerated when food is short, as the largest individual is likely to receive the lion's share and continue to grow rapidly, whilst the smallest receives barely enough to remain alive. Although the age of nestlings can be estimated by taking measurements of tarsus length or wing length, for example, and comparing these with measurements taken from birds of known age, the variation in growth rates between individuals means that this method is subject to considerable inaccuracy.

After 3-4 weeks the female no longer feeds the chicks directly and food is left on the nest for them to tear apart for themselves. Where the adults are able to bring in a surplus of food, the nest platform can become, at least from a human point of view, a decidedly unpleasant place, with swarms of flies in constant attendance and maggots crawling all over the uneaten meat. The nestlings do not seem to mind these conditions and perhaps even develop their liking for well-rotted flesh during this period. The maggots are no doubt often consumed along with the partly decomposed carcasses and the flies at least offer a target for the chicks to snap at in their more playful moments.

Despite such apparently unhygienic conditions, the chicks do at least endeavour to keep the nest free from droppings. From a very early age they perform an ungainly and somewhat comical manoeuvre that involves backing to the edge of the nest and squirting their liquid faeces out over the side. After the chicks have been in the nest for some time the ground below becomes spattered with 'whitewash'. The chicks squirt the droppings over a greater distance as they develop and, as with other birds of prey, experienced observers are able to use the amount of whitewash and the maximum distance it appears away from the nest to estimate the number and approximate age of chicks present. Although this behaviour results in a cleaner nest and probably reduces the threat from disease, it is not without its risks. A live CCTV camera at a nest in northern Scotland in 1999 caught the moment when one of the three chicks backed to the edge of the nest to perform its usual duty. As it got close to the edge it suddenly lost its balance and, despite valiant attempts to hold on, eventually fell to the ground below, leaving the remaining chicks looking somewhat bemused. Remarkably, the chick was not injured in the fall and fieldworkers were able to return it to the nest where it subsequently fledged successfully.

Fledging to independence

At about five to six weeks the chicks begin to spend much of their time standing on the nest platform, regularly spreading and flapping their wings in order to build strength in the flight muscles. There is then a gradual progression towards the first flight, which normally occurs after about 7-8 weeks in the nest. Bustamante (1993), working in southern Spain, found that the time taken to fledging for a sample of 37 chicks varied from 47 to 78 days with an average of 55 days (7.8 weeks). The variation is explained mainly by differences in the growth rates of the nestlings which is, in turn, dependent on the amount of food provided by the adults.

As the young approach fledging age they become increasingly active and adventurous, often clambering onto branches adjacent to the nest by the time they are about six weeks old. Some birds attempt their first flight before they are well enough developed to fly strongly and, by doing so, take a considerable risk. In England, chicks close to fledging age have been found on the ground near to the nest-tree on several occasions having presumably lost height when trying to fly from the nest. Here, they are vulnerable to ground predators and unless they can clamber up onto a perch, or are found during a routine nest visit, they are unlikely to survive.

Well-grown nestlings and recently fledged young have a distinctive call, quite unlike both the thin, high-pitched piping calls of small nestlings and the typical calls of full-grown birds. It is higher in pitch than the adult calls, with an upward inflection that makes it superficially similar to the call of a Curlew. It can be given singly but is often rapidly repeated, sometimes rising to an excited crescendo with the arrival of an adult carrying food.

In Doñana National Park in southern Spain, adult Red Kites aggressively chase Black Kites, Booted Eagles and Imperial Eagles, as well as individuals of their own kind that fly too close to nests with well-grown chicks or recently fledged young (Bustamante & Hiraldo 1993). A study based on prolonged observations of nest sites found that the level of aggression tended to decline during the weeks following fledging, probably because, as the young matured, they became less vulnerable to predators. The study also found that Imperial Eagles were chased more vigorously than the other species suggesting that the adult Kites viewed them as the greatest threat to their young. A leg-ring from a recently fledged Kite was found under a perch habitually used by an Imperial Eagle, showing that the threat from this species was very real (González 1989).

Recently fledged birds remain dependent on their parents for several weeks, during which time they remain close to the nest while the adults continue to bring food, either to the nest or a nearby feeding perch. Often both adults are involved in food provisioning of fledged young but, especially where food is not in short supply, this task is carried out mainly by the male and the female may spend long periods away from the nest area with little further involvement in rearing the young. This pattern of behaviour was observed at three nest sites in central England in 1999 and 2000, in two cases involving a first-year female and an adult male. It has also been regularly reported in other birds of prey including Montagu's Harrier (Clarke 1996) and Black-shouldered Kite (Newton 1979). Further study is required to determine how frequently it occurs in Red Kites.

Studies of chicks fitted with radio-transmitters in England have shown that fledglings reach independence about three to four weeks after their first flight (pers obs; Will Dixon pers comm.). Workers in southern Spain found that the post-fledging dependence period varied from as little as 11 days to a maximum of 40 days, with an average of 26 days, similar to the period found in England (Bustamante 1993). Both figures are considerably shorter than the estimate of 28-70 days given by Newton (1979). During the dependence period, the young make increasingly longer flights, progressing from short flapping flights between trees close to the nest, to soaring high above the nest wood.

The amount of food brought to the nest by the adults tends to decrease gradually during the dependence period, and young are forced to begin to find food for themselves when the supply has dried up completely. Bustamante (1993) found that young Kites in southern Spain did not start to forage for themselves until they were forced to do so, as live-capture traps, baited with meat and placed close to the nest site, failed to capture young Kites while the adults were still bringing in food. There is no evidence to suggest that young Kites ever follow the adults on foraging trips away from the nest area. The mainly scavenging lifestyle of the Kite requires no specialised hunting techniques and so, unlike many other birds of prey, the young do not need to learn how to find food from their parents.

Sex ratios

Because of the overlap in size between male and female Kites, there is no reliable means of sexing live birds other than by analysing the DNA from blood samples. All the birds taken as nestlings for the reintroduction programme in Britain were sexed in this way, as were a proportion of wild-fledged birds in the establishing populations; almost 450 birds in total. Although these birds originated from a variety of different source countries, the overall totals of 226 males and 223 females seems to confirm the expected 1:1 sex ratio that has been found in most bird of prey species that have been studied.

Human disturbance

The Kite is relatively tolerant of routine human activity away from the immediate area of the nest, and breeding territories are sometimes located close to busy roads, farmsteads and public footpaths. In these situations, the birds quickly learn to ignore routine comings and goings within sight of the nest. They are much less tolerant of human intrusion close to the nest itself and even unwitting disturbance of this kind can cause problems.

Adults often perform a very characteristic display-flight if someone approaches the nest area. It involves flying in fairly tight circles, often directly above the intruder, with exaggerated, deep flapping and a highly distinctive series of rapid, flicked wing-beats as the bird changes direction. This behaviour is usually only observed close to a nest site and often, although not always, when only a single bird is present in the air. It may serve as a form of communication between members of the pair; a means of the bird near the nest signalling to the other adult away foraging, warning of the potential disturbance and encouraging a swift return to the nest site. The display could also function as a signal to the intruder, showing that they have been spotted, and carrying the threat of attack, even if this is unlikely to be put into practice.

Human disturbance is potentially most damaging when the Kites have eggs or small chicks. If the adults are kept away from a nest for any length of time the eggs or chicks could become chilled, particularly in poor weather, and they also become more vulnerable to predation. Early on in the breeding season there is a risk that the pair may even desert a nest site completely if disturbance is frequent. In Britain, forestry operations close to a nest site are a frequently reported source of disturbance and it is recommended that, as has been suggested for Goshawks (Petty 1989), such activities are not carried out within 400m of an active nest during the breeding season.

The reaction of adult Kites to human disturbance close to the nest varies considerably. Some birds remain silent and limit their protestations to high circling above the nest area, including the deep-flapping display referred to above. Others circle very low overhead and call repeatedly for as long as the disturbance continues. Nests in England and Scotland are visited when the chicks are well-grown in order to fit rings and wing-tags. As the nest tree is climbed an adult will often circle low over the trees, sometimes even passing below the level of the canopy. On one occasion in southern England the tree climber received a considerable shock when actually struck on the back by a particularly persistent bird. At another site, Nigel Snell of the Southern England Kite Group was watching the nest tree being climbed when he was struck on the back of the head. Yarrell (1857) was in no doubt that Kites sometimes vigorously defended their nests, citing the example of a boy who climbed to a nest and received not only a severely wounded hand but also a hole in his hat before he could drive away the parent bird. Such incidents are, however, very rare.

Well-grown nestlings usually lie flat on the nest platform when there is disturbance near to the nest and can then be virtually impossible to see from the ground. If young are close to fledging age when the nest is visited then, as with the young of many other birds, there is a danger of premature fledging. This is presumably a self-defence mechanism that gives them at least a chance of survival if a predator reaches the nest and they would otherwise almost certainly be killed. It is important that nest visits are timed to avoid this period as the young have a higher chance of survival if they are left to fledge when fully ready for their first flight.

In Britain the Red Kite is listed on Schedule 1 of the Wildlife and Countryside Act (1981), making it illegal to disturb birds at or near to an active nest without the necessary licence. This protection extends from the early season through until the young are fully independent of their parents.

Breeding productivity

In most of the Kite's range, successful pairs fledge between one and four chicks with an overall average, for pairs that reach the egg-laying stage, of 1.5-2 fledged young. In mid-Wales productivity is significantly lower; a maximum of three chicks are reared and the average productivity is less than one chick for each breeding attempt (Table 12).

Table 12: **Breeding productivity of Red Kites in Europe**

Area	Young per breeding pair	Source
Southern England	2.0 (n=292)	English Nature/RSPB/Southern England Kite Group
Central England	1.6 (n=31)	English Nature/RSPB/Forest Enterprise
Northern Scotland	1.9 (n=153)	Scottish Natural Heritage/RSPB
Sweden	1.7 (n=1443)	Kjellén (1996)
Eastern Germany	1.8 (n=491)	Evans & Pienkowski (1991)
France	1.5 (n=53)	Evans & Pienkowski (1991)
Wales: 1946-90	0.7 (n=1061)	Newton, Davis & Moss (1994)
1991-98	0.9 (n=943)	Newton, Davis & Moss (1994); Welsh Kite Trust

Table 13: **Brood sizes in England, Wales and Scotland**
Welsh data for 1946-1996 (Cross & Davis 1998); English data for 1995-2000 (Southern England Kite Group/English Nature/RSPB; unpublished reports); Scottish data-RSPB/Scottish Natural Heritage

Brood size	Number of broods			Percentage		
	Wales	Scotland	England	Wales	Scotland	England
1	587	25	53	64.6	19.8	16.7
2	298	45	146	32.8	35.7	46.1
3	24	53	113	2.6	42.1	35.6
4	0	3	5	0	2.4	1.6

In Table 13 the high proportion of broods of two or three young in England and Scotland contrasts markedly with the situation in Wales where a single chick is by far the most common brood and only 2.6% of nests fledge three young. Various reasons have been suggested for the poor breeding performance in Wales including the effects of inbreeding, an unsuitable climate, food shortage resulting from the unproductive nature of the land, and interspecific competition with Buzzards and Ravens. Each of these factors is discussed in detail below.

Inbreeding
There is clear evidence from DNA analysis of blood samples that Welsh Kites show significantly less genetic variation than Kites in Continental Europe (May *et al* 1993). This is the result of the genetic bottleneck that occurred when the Welsh population was reduced to a very low level in the first half of the 20th century. There is much greater genetic variation in Kite populations in France, Spain and Germany, as numbers there were not reduced to the same extent. It has been suggested that the relatively high proportion of unhatched eggs found in Welsh nests results from a high level of inbreeding-related infertility (Cross & Davis 1998). However, other factors such as poor food supply, and hence poor condition of the breeding adults before laying, could also be responsible. Work carried out by Nick Fox, using artificial incubation, has now shown that, although some pairs do consistently produce infertile eggs, the majority of Welsh eggs are fertile and capable of producing young.

May *et al* (1993) provide two lines of evidence to suggest that inbreeding is not the most important factor in reducing productivity in Wales. Firstly, a sub-population in the south of the Welsh range showed even lower levels of genetic variation than is typical, but had significantly higher productivity than birds in the rest of the range. Secondly, blood samples taken from Swedish Kites, where the population was also reduced to a low level, revealed similar levels of inbreeding to the Welsh population (although the sample size was small) and yet productivity is relatively high (Table 12). This evidence does not rule out a negative effect due to inbreeding but does suggest that there are other factors of greater importance. It will only be possible to determine with certainty whether inbreeding has a negative effect on productivity if, in the future, inbred Welsh, and the more genetically varied reintroduced Kites are found breeding in the same areas. Productivity could then be compared in isolation from other factors relating to the currently separate breeding areas.

Competition with other species

Even a superficial review of the diet of the Kite, Buzzard and Raven suggests that there is bound to be some competition for food between the three species (Ratcliffe 1997; Tubbs 1974). Buzzards and Ravens both take carrion regularly and Buzzards hunt for small mammals that may also be taken by Kites. Buzzards occur in all the Kite areas in Britain but densities are highest in mid-Wales. Ravens are absent from central and southern England and scarce in the Scottish Kite areas, but are very common in mid-Wales. Although the reintroduced Kite populations may benefit from reduced levels of competition for food with these species, other carrion feeders such as Crows and Magpies are common throughout Britain. Elsewhere in Europe, Red Kites also face competition from these species, albeit, in the case of Buzzards and Ravens, at lower densities than are found in mid-Wales (Hagemeijer & Blair 1997).

In southern Europe, the ranges of the resident Red, and migratory Black, Kite overlap, providing considerable scope for competition between two very similar species. In southern Spain, Veiga and Hiraldo (1990) found that the diets of the two species in the breeding season were similar although there was some partitioning of foraging areas with Red Kites hunting more in areas of scrub and Black Kites spending more time in marshland habitat. Viñuela, Martí and Ruiz (1999) thought that competition with Black Kites might affect the numbers and distribution of Red Kites in Spain. Despite this possibility, breeding productivity in Spain is around double the level found in Welsh birds, strongly suggesting that factors other than competition are at work in reducing productivity in Wales.

Climate

Cross and Davis (1998) attributed 6% of nest failures in Wales to wet weather and a further 18% of failures occurred around the time of hatching when young are at their most vulnerable to adverse weather conditions. Small, down-covered chicks quickly become chilled when wet, especially when temperatures are low, and the cool and damp weather that is frequent in mid-Wales in the spring is far from ideal for rearing young.

Such conditions also have an indirect effect on the abundance of prey species, and persistent rain restricts the hunting efforts of adults, meaning that less food is brought to the nest. As a result, one of the best times to watch Kites is during a dry spell on an otherwise wet day, or on the first dry day following several rainy days. During these times the birds are often very active, keen to make the most of the opportunity to find food, having been restricted by the previous poor conditions.

Land productivity and food supply

The majority of the Kite area in mid-Wales is dominated by Silurian shale and Ordovician rock types that yield relatively infertile soils and therefore support a rather low diversity and abundance of animal life. The sub-population in southern Wales occurs in an area with more basic sandstone and limestone rocks that result in a more fertile soil and therefore sustain a greater prey base of food for Kites (May *et al* 1993). In this area, a significantly higher proportion of territorial pairs initiate breeding and a higher proportion of pairs are successful in rearing young to fledging (81.5%, n=54 against 55.7%, n=235). The improvement in breeding productivity in Wales during the last decade (see Table 12) is thought to be the result of the spread of birds into this more productive area.

Even in successful nests in mid-Wales, the majority of pairs fledge only a single chick, despite the fact that more than one egg often hatches. This again points strongly towards an impoverished food supply as an important factor influencing breeding success and is backed up by RSPB research showing that, where two chicks are present, the older bird sometimes kills its smaller sibling if food is in short supply.

A shortage of food may be the underlying reason behind breeding failures attributed to other causes. Chicks, for example, are more vulnerable to chilling in poor weather and to predation if the adults are forced to spend longer periods away from the nest in order to find food. The risk of disease is also likely to increase if chicks are malnourished as a result of a poor food supply. Lovegrove (1990) suggested that chick deaths from *Salmonella* and *Escherichia coli* bacteria in Wales were more likely when the adults brought in putrefying meat, in the absence of other, more suitable, food. The high proportion of unhatched eggs found in Welsh nests could be related to the condition of the breeding female at the time of laying, which again, is dependent on food supply. This has been shown to be the case in studies of several other birds of prey, including Buzzards, where the proportion of addled eggs in a population was lower in years with a good food supply (Newton 1979).

Breeding density

In southern England, active Kite nests have been found within 100m of each other (Evans *et al* 1999) and, in such cases, the defended area around the nest is clearly very small. In 2000, the southern England breeding area supported approximately 0.25 pairs/km^2 but this may increase in the coming years as the population continues to increase and gaps in the current range are filled. Typical densities in Wales are far lower, although there are aggregations of pairs in certain areas and active nests have been found only 200m apart in the same season.

In the northern Harz foothills in north-eastern Germany, densities of 0.3-0.5 pairs/km^2 have been recorded over a wide area and, in 1979, an incredible 136 pairs were counted in the 13km^2 Hakel Forest in this region (Nicolai 1997). The density of over 10 pairs/km^2 in this forest gives a somewhat false impression of the true abundance of Kites in the area as nests were concentrated in a central forest but birds foraged over a considerably greater area of surrounding farmland. Over recent years this population has become more dispersed with a higher number of pairs breeding in small belts of Poplars and even isolated trees in the open countryside and far fewer in the main forest. In Spain, a recent breeding survey found an average of 0.03 pairs/km^2 across large parts of the country and only very limited areas supported more than 0.2 pairs/km^2 (Viñuela, Martí & Ruiz 1999). As in the Hakel Forest, local densities were sometimes much higher as a result of the grouping of nests in isolated blocks of suitable breeding habitat.

Table 14: **Breeding densities of Red Kites in Europe**

Area	Pairs/km^2	Source
Southern England	0.25	Southern England Kite Group (Unpubl. 2000)
Northern Scotland	0.15	Scottish Natural Heritage/RSPB (Unpubl. 2000)
Harz foothills, NE Germany	0.3-0.5	Nicolai (1997)
Hakel Forest, NE Germany	10.5	Stubbe (1982)
Spain	0.03-0.16	Viñuela, Martí & Ruiz (1999)
Austria	0.05-0.2	Gamauf (1995)
Corsica	1.5-2.0	Mougeot (2000)

Chapter 9

SOCIAL BEHAVIOUR AND PLAY

The Red Kite is unusual, although by no means unique, among birds of prey in its highly gregarious nature, particularly outside the breeding season. Throughout the range, communal winter roosting is typical and the majority of birds across a large area may use the same roost site each evening. In areas with a healthy resident or wintering population, gatherings involving several hundred birds are not uncommon, forming one of the most impressive bird of prey spectacles in Europe. Several theories have been put forward in an attempt to explain the benefits of such behaviour, including defence against predators, improved foraging efficiency and as a means of meeting potential future mates.

There is often a significant amount of social interaction between birds gathering at roost sites and this includes behaviour which is best described as play, as it seems to serve no immediately useful purpose. On some evenings, spectacular aerial chases take place, with birds diving at each other and sometimes almost interlocking talons in mock fights before separating again. Play is common during roost gatherings probably because, in late afternoon, birds that have found sufficient food earlier in the day have time on their hands before they move to the final roosting location at dusk.

The communal roost

The social nature of the Red Kite is best appreciated by visiting a major communal roost site on a winter's afternoon. During the latter part of the afternoon a slow trickle of birds gradually increases until single birds and small groups are arriving almost constantly from all directions. The birds are drawn together on arrival in the area, either perching in groups in prominent trees along a hedgeline or at the edge of the wood, or wheeling and chasing together over the roost area. New arrivals are frequently greeted by calling from, particularly adult, birds that are already present. All such behaviour is loosely termed pre-roosting and many individuals do not move to their final resting place for the night, usually well within a woodland and out of sight, until the light is beginning to fade. Some late arrivals even slip into the roost wood when it is almost completely dark.

Patterns of behaviour during pre-roost gatherings are strongly influenced by the weather. Aerial activity, for example, is greatly increased when there is a moderate to strong wind, presumably because the birds are able to fly more efficiently, with less expenditure of energy, in such conditions. On calm afternoons, the birds arriving in the roost area are more likely to remain perched in prominent trees for long periods. The attendance patterns of individual birds vary, probably depending on foraging success during the day. Birds arriving at the roost in near darkness are likely to be those that have struggled to find food and have made the most of all available daylight in order to continue foraging. The bulging crops of some of the birds arriving in the roost area in daylight, clearly visible as they pass overhead, show that they have fed recently.

Once most birds are settled in their final roosting position as dusk approaches, there is a significant reduction in visible activity. The late arrivals often head directly to the perch where they will spend the night as there is little daylight left in which to indulge in the usual pre-roosting activities. At this stage, the perched birds are sensitive to disturbance within or close to the roost wood and, although they will tolerate someone walking quietly, even very close to the wood, a sudden, unexpected noise can send all the gathered birds back up into the air.

On one memorable clear and still early evening at a roost site in southern England, just as the sun was finally disappearing behind the low Chiltern hills, a loud clattering noise from a nearby farmyard disturbed upwards of 100 Kites from their perches within a small wood. They rose above the wood, initially in a tight group, but gradually fanning out over a wider area of the surrounding countryside, before returning, in small groups, to resettle in trees close to the original roost. In central England, disturbance caused by pigeon shooting late in the afternoon has resulted in a sudden change of the final roosting location as all the gathered birds have flown up and drifted several hundred metres to a different group of trees. At this site, the birds now have a number of alternative blocks of woodland that are regularly used for roosting, all within an area of about 2km². The final selection on each evening is, at times, governed by disturbance factors, but often seems to be random. The location chosen by the first few birds to settle is probably simply copied by later arrivals. In Spain, it is apparently common for the majority of birds assembled at a roost to rise into the air *en masse* a few times before finally settling for the night and this behaviour provides an ideal opportunity to count the number of birds using the roost (Viñuela 1997). Using this method, counts of up to 500 birds have been made at sites in northern Spain.

Departures from roost sites in the morning follow a similar pattern to arrivals, with singles and small groups leaving at intervals from first light onwards. The birds that leave soon after first light may be those that struggled to find food during the previous day and are therefore keen to resume foraging at the earliest opportunity. As in the evening, birds leaving the roost sometimes call to each other, presumably so that groups of birds can keep together as they head off to begin foraging (see under 'network foraging'). Continuous rain or dense fog tends to prolong the period spent in the roost area as such conditions are far from ideal for active foraging. If the wet or foggy weather persists then some birds may remain in, or close to, the roost for the whole day.

In many Kite areas the requirement for an area of woodland not subject to frequent human disturbance is satisfied by a large number of different sites, and it is not known why particular woods are selected for roosting and then used repeatedly for many years. Such sites perhaps become established as traditional roosts through birds in each generation simply following the example of older birds that are already familiar with the location. In central England, the first birds released at the start of the reintroduction project in 1995 eventually settled on an area about 8km away from the release site. Radio-tracking and direct observation showed that the same block of woodland was used for roosting every night throughout the winter and, in subsequent years, each new group of released and, more recently, wild-fledged, young have come to use the same roost. The site is still by far the most important roost in the area and now regularly attracts over 50 birds in winter. In southern England, where the population exceeds 500 birds, there are a number of alternative roost sites and radio-tracking carried out by Peter Stevens has shown that some birds move between sites regularly during the winter. The initial site, used by the majority of birds when the population was considerably smaller, still regularly attracts well over 100 birds. Radio-tracking has revealed a similar pattern of behaviour in southern Spain where wintering birds from central Europe utilise numerous different roost sites during the course of a winter (Heredia, Alonso & Hiraldo 1991).

The distance between active roosts varies with local population density and, to a lesser extent, with time of year. In central Spain, the distance between adjacent roost sites varied from 3.6 to 10km in areas with high numbers of wintering birds, and there was evidence that birds tended to concentrate in fewer, larger, roosts later in the winter (Viñuela 1992). In Britain, roosts are usually more fragmented and less predictable in autumn and early winter, with numbers at the most important sites building up from late August or September to a peak in the November-February period when weather conditions are usually most severe. Roosts generally begin to break up in late February-March as birds start to move away to potential breeding sites.

Communal gatherings of young, non-breeding, birds occur throughout the summer but these are not as predictable or site-faithful as is the case in winter.

Composition of roost gatherings

In England, some established pairs remain on their breeding territories throughout the winter and are only seen infrequently at communal pre-roost gatherings. The roosts are dominated by birds of the year and birds in their second winter, the majority of which have yet to make their first breeding attempt. Adults from nest sites within a few kilometres of the communal roost also regularly attend pre-roost gatherings but it is not known if, on these occasions, they subsequently roost communally or return to their breeding site to roost.

In Wales and northern Scotland more of the breeding adults tend to join roosts, perhaps because, in these areas, food is less easy to come by on the breeding territory during winter. Some return sporadically to their breeding site, particularly in fine weather from January onwards. In southern Spain, Heredia, Alonso and Hiraldo (1991) used radio-tracking to highlight differences in roosting behaviour between wintering birds from central Europe and the resident breeding population. Wintering Kites (both adults and first-years) gathered at communal roosts of 5-80 individuals, where they were sometimes joined by immature birds from the resident population. In contrast, the resident breeding adults almost always roosted in their nest tree or its immediate vicinity.

A group of Kites pre-roosting in a hedgeline tree. Birds typically perch facing into the wind, presumably in order to avoid their feathers being unduly ruffled

Dan Powell

Network foraging

One of the main potential benefits of joining a communal roost is the chance to improve foraging efficiency by learning about new food sources from other birds attending the roost. The 'information centre' theory (Ward & Zahavi 1973) suggests that birds are able to improve their chances of finding food by following other, more knowledgeable, individuals from a roost or colony. Although this has been demonstrated to occur in only a very small number of bird species, including the Cliff Swallow and American Black Vulture, it has been suggested that the same mechanism may operate at Red Kite roosts. In winter, Kites frequently feed on mammal or bird carcasses that are large enough to provide food for several individuals and may remain as a suitable food source for several days. In theory, it would therefore be possible for an individual that has struggled to find food, to follow a more successful bird from the roost on the following day in order to locate a carcass at which to feed.

In order to test the 'information centre' theory, Hiraldo, Heredia and Alonso (1993) studied a group of radio-tagged Red Kites and their foraging behaviour in southern Spain. They found that, although Kites fed at carcasses large enough to be shared, these usually lasted for only a single day and following successful birds from the roost was therefore unlikely to lead directly to a known food source. This was backed up by observations of radio-tagged birds departing from the roost in the morning. The birds often left the roost in small groups, but there appeared to be no obvious leader and birds known to have fed well during the previous day were not followed. This study suggested that an alternative food finding strategy termed 'network foraging' (Mock, Lamey & Thomson 1988) fitted the observed patterns of behaviour more convincingly and provided a valid explanation of why communal roosting was beneficial. According to this strategy, it is worthwhile for a bird to leave the roost as part of a loose group so that when one individual is successful in locating a new food source, the others can quickly converge to share in the discovery. Each bird in the group effectively improves its chances of finding food and, as carcasses are often large enough to feed several birds, there is no disadvantage to the finder in having to share. Gathering at communal roosts is advantageous as it ensures that sufficient birds are available at the start of the following day for social foraging to be possible.

Other benefits of communal roosting

Several reasons not connected with improved foraging efficiency have been suggested for the communal roosting habits of Kites, although there is currently little concrete evidence available to support them. Some bird species are known to conserve heat by communal roosting. Small passerines, with their high surface area to volume ratio, are particularly vulnerable to cold winter conditions and often roost huddled together for warmth. Larger birds rarely roost together for this purpose, at least in temperate climates, and it is highly unlikely that the Kite is an exception to this rule. In central England, when roosts were visited on moonlit nights, groups of birds could be seen perched close together in several adjacent trees but not in such close proximity as to suggest that they were trying to conserve heat. It is also the case that, in many areas, breeding adults roost solitarily close to their nest sites throughout the year and have no problems surviving even the harshest weather conditions.

Many birds roost and forage in flocks in order to reduce the risk of predation. With more pairs of eyes there is a better chance that approaching predators will be detected and the chance of a successful attack is reduced. It is hard to believe that full-grown Kites are sufficiently vulnerable to predators to make communal roosting worthwhile for this purpose and adult Kites that roost solitarily, together with many other solitary roosting raptors, do not seem to suffer significant losses. The anti-predator explanation for communal roosting is more appropriate for ground-roosting species such as harriers where there is a much higher risk of predation (e.g. Clarke 1996).

For a species that normally pairs for life, finding an appropriate mate is clearly important and communal gatherings offer an ideal opportunity to size up the potential. Aerial displays involving two first-year birds are frequently seen during pre-roost gatherings and it is possible that these sometimes involve a male and female in the early stages of pair-bonding. One highly distinctive display involves two birds flying close together, one close behind the other, with both using exaggerated deep, slow, wing-beats. In the breeding season, this same display between adults has been interpreted as essentially aggressive as it is sometimes followed by a rapid chase, but it may also have a role in strengthening the bond between two paired birds. It is unlikely that communal roosts form primarily to facilitate behaviour of this nature but, once established, it is inevitable that unpaired birds will mix and they no doubt make the most of the opportunity to socialise.

Social behaviour and distribution

The Kite's distribution across its European range is noticeably patchy, with pockets of high density, close to areas where Kites are seen only infrequently. The reasons for this include differences in habitat suitability, food supply and intensity of persecution but, at times, these explanations do not seem entirely adequate. Areas with very few Kites sometimes have a very similar landscape and management regime to an adjacent area supporting a high-density population.

Although persecution is usually the main reason that Kite populations become fragmented in the first place, the benefits derived from social gatherings probably help to prevent a more rapid recolonisation of areas that are now free from such threats. Young birds are reluctant to settle in an area where few Kites are present as they would then be unable to benefit from group foraging and the other social activities that take place at communal roosts. As a result, traditional roosts increase in size until the amount of food available locally imposes an upper limit on numbers and birds are then forced to explore further afield. Recolonisation is therefore likely to occur gradually with Kites moving out little by little from areas of high population density.

It is not clear whether network foraging operates to some extent during the breeding season. Home ranges certainly overlap and although most birds seem to forage alone, it is possible that they learn about important food sources by observing other birds in the area. This could be one reason for the clustered pattern of breeding pairs found in parts of the range and, together with the tendency of young birds to breed close to their natal site, may further reduce the rate of spread into unoccupied but suitable habitats.

Play

Two main forms of play activity are seen frequently in Kites, each with a number of variations on a similar theme. The first involves using outstretched talons to snatch at objects or vegetation in flight. At the main communal roost in central England this behaviour has been observed on a number of occasions, involving individual Kites snatching foliage both from near to ground level and from the thin upper branches of deciduous trees. On one winter evening, a single bird was watched flying low above a crop of Oilseed Rape and grabbing at the leaves of the crop, only a few inches from the ground. The behaviour was repeated several times with the leaves grabbed and then dropped fairly rapidly on each occasion. At the same site, Kites have also been observed snatching foliage from the outer branches of trees, repeatedly dropping and re-catching the same leafy twig in flight. Each time the twig is dropped, the bird folds back its wings in order to lose height rapidly, preventing it from falling more than a few metres towards the ground.

Kites are often seen picking up objects from the ground and flying with them for a short period before dropping and then re-catching them again. On some occasions, this is no doubt a genuine attempt to detect food and the object is then quickly discarded as soon as the bird realises that it is inedible. At other times, such behaviour must be regarded as play as the same object, clearly of no food value, is repeatedly picked up and dropped. If other Kites are nearby they often join in with the game, chasing each other and intercepting the object in mid-air if it is dropped by the leading bird. Encalado (1998) watched several Red Kites at a rubbish dump in Zamora, Spain playing with a piece of newspaper. A pursuing bird managed to snatch the paper from the talons of the initial owner and was, itself, then immediately chased by two other birds. In central England, dried sheep droppings are a favoured play object and other materials have included wool, sticks and pieces of plastic and rubber. Sticks are often carried by first-year, non-breeding birds in spring and can lead to erroneous claims of nest building. They are, however, usually quickly dropped rather than carried away to a nest site.

The second main form of play activity involves aerial chases and mock fights between two or more birds. This is regularly seen at pre-roost gatherings, particularly on breezy days when the birds are able to use the wind to fly with minimal expenditure of energy. In central England, up to 40 birds have been watched circling together above the roost wood with frenetic chases between individuals occurring at regular intervals. Walters Davies and Davis (1973) coined the term 'circus' to describe such gatherings in Wales. Chases may develop into mock fights as one bird dives towards another with talons outstretched, and the other bird responds by rolling onto its back and thrusting out its own talons in defence. It sometimes appears as if the two birds must surely collide but direct contact is rare and the birds usually rejoin the circling group after only a brief bout of sparring. Where chases are more prolonged they frequently involve high-speed changes of direction as the leading bird twists and turns ahead of its pursuer with remarkable agility. This sort of interaction can be rather surprising if one is familiar with the Kite's usual leisurely, gliding flight as it drifts across open country in search of food.

The concept of play activity as a means of learning or improving skills is a familiar one in the mammal world but there are far fewer documented examples involving birds. Nevertheless, there is every reason to suppose that the benefits of play are much the same for both groups. A clue to this learning role for play in Kites is the prevalence of such activity in immature birds. Most of the examples described above from central England involved birds in their first year that had yet to make their first breeding attempt. The same pattern is found in mammals where it is the young and inexperienced individuals that most commonly indulge in play, as a means of learning behaviour important in later adult life.

Both of the main types of play seen in Kites have close parallels with forms of behaviour that are genuinely useful and it is easy to see how play could contribute to an individual's survival prospects by improving coordination or flying agility.

Playing with objects, including the snatching of vegetation, could help to improve both feeding techniques and nest building skills. One of the Kite's most frequent foraging techniques involves flying down to grab an animal carcass or piece of carrion from the ground without pausing to land. This is clearly a difficult skill as birds sometimes swoop down and reach out with their talons, only to miss the intended target. Play no doubt helps birds to improve their success rate through repeated practice. Breeding is dependent on the collection of enough suitable nest material, either from the ground or, in some cases, sticks broken from a living tree. Here again, there are clear parallels with play involving objects, including sticks, seen in birds of pre-breeding age.

Aerial chases and mock fights in young birds are almost identical to behaviour used by breeding adults in order to defend the area around their nest site. Anything that improves agility must be of help in driving away a rival male or a potential nest predator, for example. Flying skills are also important in attracting a mate in the first place as display flights are thought to be an important part of courtship behaviour.

Interaction with corvids

Skills learnt during play are also of direct benefit when fending off the unwelcome attentions of corvids, an all too frequent activity for Kites in many areas. Most birds of prey are, at times, mobbed by corvids but the Kite, with its slow foraging flights, often low over the ground, is perhaps a particularly appealing target. Jackdaws, Rooks and Carrion Crows seem never to tire of the activity and sometimes a group of ten or more will gang up on an individual Kite, forming a long, straggling tail behind the hapless bird. If the harrying becomes too intense, the Kite may suddenly roll over in flight and turn towards the birds with talons outstretched, an action that has only a short-term effect and rarely prevents the mobbing birds from continuing with their harassment. A more successful strategy is simply to land in a tree and wait. The pursuing corvids often land in the same tree but will not risk perching too close and so the Kite is left in relative peace, at least until it takes to the wing once more.

Mobbing birds may view a large bird of prey as a threat, particularly in summer when they have nestlings or recently fledged young, and the act of mobbing is then a genuine attempt to drive the bird away. At other times, the mobsters are more interested in a bird with food and their behaviour is designed to inconvenience the bird sufficiently for it to drop whatever it is carrying. William Blundell writing in the 17th century (quoted by Mitchell 1892), was well aware of the hostility between corvids and Kites, and how such behaviour could be exploited by those wishing to trap and kill Crows:

[if you] take a Kite and a Carrion-Crow, and tie them down in the stubble with sufficient liberty, they will fight and cry in a strange manner: upon which there will come immediately great flocks of Crows from all parts, which, striking freely at the Kite, will many of them be taken in the lime twig which must be placed round in the stubble for that reason.

Corvids often mob a Kite that is not carrying food and, in attempting to retreat, is clearly signalling that it has no aggressive intentions. It is easy to believe that, in these situations, it is the corvids that are indulging in play activity, perhaps in preparation for the time when they have young, and sparring between the species becomes an altogether more serious business.

Chapter 10

HOME RANGE AND DISPERSAL

The size of the Red Kite's home range during the breeding season and in winter, together with patterns of dispersal, vary across the bird's range, influenced by factors such as climate, landscape and food supply. In ideal habitat in England, where food is abundant and winters are mild, home ranges are fairly small and adult birds do not stray far from their breeding site throughout the year.

In resident populations, some young birds remain in the natal area for their whole life, while others disperse during their first autumn or in the following spring, often travelling well away from their birthplace. Dispersal differs from migration in that it involves movements, mainly by first-year birds, which are exploratory in nature and unpredictable, with considerable variation in direction and distance travelled between individuals. Migration (covered in Chapter 4) involves regular, repeated, and, to a large extent, predictable, movements between separate breeding and wintering areas.

Home range

As Red Kites do not defend an exclusive feeding area from others of their own kind, even during the breeding season, home range, rather than territory, is the most appropriate term for the area they make use of. The focal point for the home range during the breeding season is the nest site, whilst in winter, adults either remain close to their breeding site or, if food becomes more difficult to find, move away to a more productive area.

It is only possible to define home ranges accurately by carrying out intensive studies of radio-tagged birds. In Britain this has been done mostly with first-year Kites as radio-tags are fitted to nestlings before they fledge or to young birds released as part of the reintroduction programme, and often do not last into adulthood. For adults, rough estimates of home range have been made based on observations of individually identifiable wing-tagged birds.

Breeding season

The home range utilised by breeding pairs for foraging varies markedly with the local availability of food. In Wales, Walters Davies and Davis (1973) found that individuals normally ranged up to 2-3km from the nest site, although, in some cases, individually marked birds were recorded as far as 15km away from their nest. In Germany, Ortlieb (1989) thought that foraging flights of up to 10km from nests were typical and in southern Spain, Veiga and Hiraldo (1990) recorded feeding trips of up to 20km away from nests. These, however, represent extreme distances and the adults no doubt found the majority of food from much closer to the nest site. Direct observations of the male Kite from a breeding pair near Göttingen, central Germany, showed that the maximum distance travelled from the nest was 4.5km and the majority of foraging flights were within 2.5km of the nest (Porstendörfer 1997). Almost all flights were within an arc of approximately 180° on the eastern side of the nest site and the total home range in which the bird located food for itself and its nestlings was a relatively limited 7.5km².

In high quality habitat in England, where breeding success is high, sightings of wing-tagged birds show that adults find most of their food within about 3km of the nest and are only rarely seen further than 5km from a nest with eggs or chicks. Figure 6 is based on 51 records of individually marked birds seen at least 1km away from their nest site during the breeding season. Almost all the records involve males as females were only very rarely recorded more than 1km from their breeding site. It is interesting to note that eight out of the nine records where birds were seen more than 4km from the nest involved a single pair, in a year when they had moved 5km from their previous nest site. Despite this change of breeding site, the male was regularly seen foraging over land close to the previous year's nest site, requiring far longer flights from the nest than is usual. It was presumably advantageous for this bird to make use of foraging areas with which it was familiar from the previous year, despite the longer distance foraging flights required. What is less clear is why the pair moved to a new nest site well away from a foraging area that was obviously so highly favoured.

Figure 6: **Foraging distances from nest sites in central England**

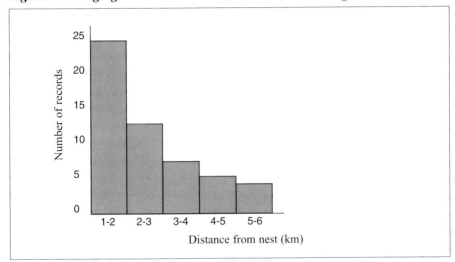

Within most home ranges there will be habitats such as mature woodland and well-grown arable crops that are unsuitable for foraging. The area actually utilised by the pair will therefore be smaller than initially suggested by the total size of the home range. Radio transmitters with a battery life of three years have now been fitted to nestlings in England and should allow a much more detailed assessment of the size and patterns of use of home ranges utilised by breeding adults. Initial work carried out by Will Dixon and Deborah Ottway suggests that the estimates of typical distances birds travel from the nest in order to find food, based on sightings of wing-tagged birds, are reasonably accurate.

Winter

The communal roost becomes the focal point of the home range for many birds in winter, particularly for individuals that have yet to breed and for adults that winter away from their breeding area. Some individuals utilise a fairly restricted area around a single roost, returning every evening to the same site, whilst others wander more widely, visiting several different roosts and making use of a far larger area during the course of a winter.

Radio-tracking of first-year Kites in England over several winters showed that the majority of foraging took place within 4km of the single roost site used by all immature birds in the population (Carter & Grice 2000). Within this radius of the roost, some areas were used far more frequently than others, presumably according to the amount of food available. Home ranges determined for six individuals, each based on at least 30 locations, ranged from 19 to 32km², with an average of 23km². As is clear from the examples plotted in Figure 7, within each home range are areas used more frequently than would be expected by chance. This is partly the result of local differences in food availability but is also influenced by the preferences of individual birds. The bird in Figure 7(a) clearly favoured an area to the west and northwest of the roost site, whereas the bird in 7(c) spent little time in this area and was recorded more often to the south of the roost.

Because Kites do not defend an exclusive territory from others of their own kind they are not restricted to a specific range with strict boundaries and are therefore able to exploit different areas opportunistically during the winter if patterns of food availability change. An intensive programme of Rabbit control on a particular farm, for example, may turn an area formerly lacking in animal carrion into a highly productive foraging area. Similarly, the beginning of the Pheasant-shooting season might provide a sudden abundance of carrion on estates where shooting is frequent, drawing in Kites from the surrounding countryside.

In this respect, Kites have a degree of flexibility that is not the case in more strictly territorial species such as the Buzzard. In a high density population of Buzzards studied by Robin Prytherch in southwest England, territories are often smaller than 1km² and these are resolutely defended throughout the year. Food must be found within this restricted area as, if an individual strays into a neighbouring territory, it is likely to be quickly driven away by the resident adults.

In Doñana, southern Spain there is a contrast in ranging behaviour between birds wintering in the area from breeding grounds in central Europe and the local resident adults (Heredia, Alonso & Hiraldo 1991). A radio-tracking study showed that the resident adults used comparatively small home ranges in winter, centred on their nest sites where they returned to roost each night. Individual home ranges varied from 6.5 to 36km² with a median value for six different individuals of 29km². The core home ranges, defined as those areas used more frequently than would be expected by chance, varied from as little as 2.7 up to 11.5km², with a median value of 3.6km².

Figure 7: **Winter home ranges for three first-year Red Kites in central England, Oct-Feb, 1996-97.** *(The grid is made up of 1km squares and each dot represents a location determined by radio-tracking.)*

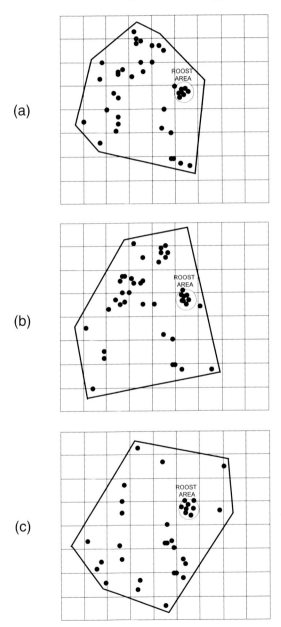

In the same area, wintering Kites from central Europe roosted communally and tended to utilise larger home ranges than the resident birds. The overall home ranges for a sample of eight birds varied from 15 to 42km^2 and core ranges varied from 4.3 to 14.5km^2, with a median value of 6km^2. As would be expected from the larger home ranges, wintering birds also tended to be found further away from their roost sites during the day, averaging 5.8km when located by radio-tracking, compared with an average of 3.9km for the resident birds. This clear difference in behaviour is probably a reflection of the greater knowledge of the local area by breeding adults with established home ranges. Through familiarity with a relatively small area around the nest site they are able to find sufficient food for themselves, without resorting to social foraging. Wintering migrant birds do not enjoy such familiarity with their surroundings but can improve their chances of finding food by foraging in loose groups.

Movements of immatures

Even in resident Kite populations a proportion of the young fledged each year undertake dispersive movements away from their birthplace. These movements tend to be initiated in either the autumn, soon after they have become independent, or in the following spring, and during the intervening winter period birds usually remain settled in the same area. In this respect the Red Kite differs from the closely related, but highly migratory, Black Kite, whose young move away from the nest almost as soon as they are independent (Bustamante & Hiraldo 1993). As shown in Table 15, dispersive movements take place in all directions and, in some cases, over very large distances.

The most unexpected movement so far recorded involved a first-year Kite from the reintroduced population in northern Scotland. This individual fledged in July 1997 and was recorded in Iceland in December of the same year having under-taken a remarkable flight of more than 1000km across the North Atlantic. Most large birds of prey avoid crossing expanses of water wherever possible, as the rising thermals used in order to gain height are much stronger over land. This individual may have become caught up in high-altitude winds that carried it north from Scotland, rather than deliberately setting out to fly in this direction. It survived two harsh Icelandic winters, helped by handouts of food from a local farmer, before being found covered in Fulmar oil and flown back to Scotland for rehabilitation. After a period of quarantine and convalescence, the bird was released back into the wild in northern Scotland in March 2000. The story did not ultimately have a happy ending as, six weeks later, it was it was found dead 42km away from the release point.

Table 15: Long distance movements of British Red Kites

Information for reintroduced populations from English Nature/Scottish Natural Heritage/RSPB project newsletters/reports. Welsh records from Welsh Kite Trust newsletters and Cross & Davis (1998)

Area of origin	Release (R) or Fledging (F) date	Location and date recorded	Distance/ direction travelled	Comments
Southern England	July 1990 (R)	15km NE of Rouen, France: January 1991	290km SE	Found dead, from unknown causes, after severe storms
Southern England	July 1993 (F)	Near Brussels, Belgium: December 1997	c.400km ESE	Found dead from unknown causes
Central England	July 1997 (R)	Near Holywell, north Wales: July 1997	200km WNW	Found dead under powerlines only two weeks after being released. One of six birds released in central England to be recorded in Wales during their first winter, mostly associating with Welsh Kites
Central England	July 1997 (R)	Gouthwaite Reservoir, North Yorkshire: October to December 1997	210km NNW	Not recorded after December 1997
Suffolk	July 1997 (F)	The Netherlands: November 1998	c.150km E	Previously recorded at a west Wales feeding site. The two other young fledged from this nest also dispersed, one to central Wales and the other to join Kites in southern England
Central Wales	July 1970 (F)	Wrotham. Nr. Maidstone, Kent: August 1970	315km ESE	Found dead on railway line. A small proportion of young Welsh Kites probably disperse into England each year
Central Wales	Late June 1992 (F)	Gas rig off north Norfolk coast, 45km off Cromer: 19th July 1992	390km ENE	Surprisingly early date for such a long distance movement by a recently fledged bird
Central Wales	July 1995 (F)	Ballyvaldon, Wexford, Ireland: 20th October 1999	c.200km ENE	Found dead. First overseas recovery of a Welsh ringed Kite
Northern Scotland	July 1995 (F)	Stokenchurch, Oxfordshire: Late January and March 1996	720km SSE	Seen at southern England communal roost. Also recorded in North Yorkshire and the central England communal roost before returning to its natal area in northern Scotland to breed
Northern Scotland	July 1997 (F)	Cape Clear Island, Co Cork, Ireland: October 1997	820km SW	An estimated 10% of Scottish first-year Kites cross to Ireland each autumn
Northern Scotland	July 1997 (F)	Iceland: December 1997 to November 1999	1,020km NW	See text
Northern Scotland	July 1998 (F)	Vizcaya, near Bilbao, Spain: May 1999	1,600km S	Found dead under powerlines
Central Scotland	July 1997 (R)	Elkstone, Gloucestershire: February 1998	506km SSE	Birds released in Scotland have wintered in Northern and southern Ireland, and central Wales as well as in England. This individual had returned to the release area by mid-May 1998

The majority of movements are not as extreme as the examples in Table 15 and, in resident populations, most young birds remain close to their natal site rather than dispersing. Many of the birds that do disperse, subsequently return to the area where they were born (or released) having been away for anything from a few days to almost two years.

As would be expected from these examples of long distance movements, Kites fledged elsewhere in Europe sometimes end up in Britain, either briefly as passage migrants or, far less often, as permanent recruits into one of the British populations. Although such movements usually go undetected, there are a few records from individually marked birds that have been recovered in Britain, including at least six German ringed birds (Toms & Clark 1998). These include an individual fledged in Schleswig-Holstein in June 1971 that was found dead at Pantydwr near Rhayader in July 1972, probably as a result of poisoning (Walters Davies & Davis 1973), and a bird ringed in Sachsen that was found in Essex about one year after it had fledged.

In the re-establishing populations in Britain, the proportion of youngsters that disperse tends to decrease as population size increases. Thus, there has been a significantly greater loss of birds released at sites in England and Scotland in the early years of reintroduction projects (Carter & Grice 2000; Evans *et al* 1999). The figures below show how, in northern Scotland, the proportion of released birds that moved more than 50km away from the area decreased as the project progressed:

$$1989 - 100\%; \quad n=6$$
$$1990 - 79\%; \quad n=19$$
$$1991 - 60\%; \quad n=20$$
$$1992 - 38\%; \quad n=24$$
$$1993 - 25\%; \quad n=24$$

Between 60 and 100% of birds dispersed in the early years before a population had become established. But in 1993, when the population had increased to 12 territorial pairs, only 25% of released birds dispersed. The release area clearly became a more attractive proposition for young birds once it supported a reasonable population as a result of previous releases, reflecting the inherently social nature of the species.

For reasons that are not fully understood, the proportion of birds moving away from the release areas has been higher in Scotland than in England and this is one of the reasons why population growth has been more rapid in England. It is unlikely that this is the result of differences in food supply as survival rates for birds remaining close to the release sites are very high and there appears to be no shortage of food in any of the release areas. This is particularly true in the early stages of a project when intraspecific competition is low as a result of the small number of Kites in the area. It is also unclear why, when a group of birds are all released in the same place and at the same time, some disperse whilst others remain in the release area. It is likely that the tendency to disperse is at least partly governed by the genetic make up of individuals. If this is so then the fact that birds released in Scotland were taken from largely migratory populations in Sweden and Germany, whereas those released in England came mostly from resident populations in Spain, may help to explain the differences in behaviour.

Figure 8: **Records of Kites in central England that dispersed more than 20km away from their release site, 1995-98**

Natal philopatry

Young Red Kites show a strong tendency to breed for the first time close to the site where they themselves were reared. This applies even to individuals that disperse away from their birthplace, as many subsequently return to the natal area before they reach breeding age. Faithfulness to the natal site is shown well by the large number of Welsh birds that have been marked as chicks and subsequently found breeding. Of 139 birds recorded in this way, the average distance moved from birthplace to breeding site was only about 12.5km (Cross & Davis 1998).

In the southern England reintroduction area, Kites have been slow to recolonise nearby vacant habitat even though breeding productivity within the highest density parts of the range has declined (Peter Stevens in litt), probably due to interference between adjacent pairs and increasing competition for food. As densities increase further, productivity may continue to fall and age of first breeding may rise as it becomes more difficult for young adults to find an unoccupied nesting site or sufficient food to reach breeding condition. From a human perspective it seems nonsensical that young adults in this situation do not simply move to ideal, but currently unoccupied, habitat where there is no competition for food or shortage of nest sites. However, by returning to the area where it was born and fledged successfully, a young Kite is selecting an area that it knows with certainty must provide suitable habitat. Without actually making a breeding attempt there may be no reliable means of assessing the suitability of other areas, particularly areas where other Kites are not present, and an individual risks wasting valuable resources if it decides to take a chance. Natal philopatry no doubt evolved long before human persecution became a significant factor, when there were unlikely to be significant areas of unoccupied but suitable breeding habitat available.

There are exceptions to the general pattern of faithfulness to the natal site and a few of the more adventurous birds do end up breeding well away from their own birthplace. Usually such movements are from one Kite population to another and there are several examples of birds from the reintroduced populations in England and Scotland that have bred away from the population where they were reared or released. A bird fledged in northern Scotland has bred in central Scotland and there has been recruitment in both directions between the central and southern England populations, only about 100km apart. So far, the only bird from one of the reintroduced populations that has been recorded breeding in central Wales was a female released in central England in 1997 and found dead on a nest in Wales in spring 2000. There are no proven examples of Welsh birds breeding in England or Scotland although, as Welsh young are no longer fitted with wing-tags, such movements could easily have taken place without being detected.

It is strongly suspected that Continental birds have recruited into both the southern England and Welsh populations. In both cases evidence from the analysis of DNA in blood samples has shown that genetic traits found in central European Kites are now present in these two British populations (May, Wetton & Parkin 1993; Ian Evans pers comm.).

It is much more unusual for Kites that move away from their birthplace to end up breeding away from other established populations. This may be partly due to lack of opportunity, as a wandering bird is unlikely to meet up with a bird of the opposite sex in unoccupied habitat, and partly for the reasons discussed above, relating to the social nature of the species. Occasionally, however, isolated breeding pairs do become established. In eastern England an isolated pair bred in northeast Suffolk for two consecutive years in 1996 and 1997, rearing a total of five young. It was thought most likely that the adults were migrants from the Continent that, for whatever reason, settled in the area to breed (Carter 1998). It was hoped that a small population might become established but the pair did not breed again in 1998 and all the young from the previous two years dispersed away from the nest site (see Table 15). It seems that, for these young birds, the instinct to want to breed in an area already supporting a well-established Kite population proved stronger than the instinct to return to breed at the natal site.

In the last few years several other isolated pairs, involving birds from the reintroduction programme, have bred in southern counties of England. As yet there are no signs that this will lead to the establishment of new populations away from the release areas and population expansion continues to be mainly by a gradual spread from the main core of breeding birds.

Movements of adults

Very few adults in resident populations undertake long-distance movements once they have bred for the first time, although such behaviour is occasionally recorded following a breeding failure. This is a sensible strategy and one that is followed by many long-lived birds as, by remaining in the same area, individuals benefit from their knowledge of the surroundings. Their chances of surviving a period of poor winter weather or of rearing chicks successfully in the breeding season are improved by knowing, through experience, where food and shelter are most likely to be found.

Variation between the sexes

All young birds released in England and Scotland have been sexed by analysing the DNA in blood samples. As a result of monitoring their movements following release, differences in dispersal behaviour between the sexes have become apparent. Evans *et al* (1999) analysed the movements of 73 birds released in southern England and 92 birds released in northern Scotland. In England, 29% of males and 53% of females moved more than 50km away from the release site in their first year, while in Scotland, the equivalent figures were 42% for males and 57.5% for females. In central England there was a similar disparity between the sexes leading to an eventual excess of males in the population despite the fact that more females than males were released (Carter & Grice 2000).

In most species where there is a greater tendency for females to disperse, it is the males that are responsible for establishing breeding territories in order to attract a female (Campbell & Lack 1985) and this does appear to be the case with the Red Kite. In this situation males increase their chances of successfully establishing a territory and attracting a female if they remain in one area, becoming as familiar as possible with the locality and its most productive foraging areas. Females, with no such responsibilities, are free to explore further afield, perhaps on the lookout for alternative breeding opportunities in other areas.

Adult females tend to utilise smaller home ranges than males during the breeding season and this is not surprising given the male bird's greater responsibility for food provisioning. To find that such a difference is maintained during the winter is perhaps less expected but there is evidence that this might be the case from an intensive radio-tracking study in southern Spain (Heredia, Alonso & Hiraldo 1991). Although the study was based on a sample of only two males and three females it found that males ranged further from their winter roost sites and utilised significantly larger home ranges than females. It was suggested that, by not ranging as widely as males during the winter, females were better able to build up fat reserves for the forthcoming breeding season. This could be very important as, during incubation and the early chick period, females are restricted to the nest site and must rely mainly on food that the male is able to provide. It is also possible that, being confined to the nest and its immediate vicinity for a substantial part of the breeding season, the female does not develop as large a home range as the male, choosing to rely on the area with which she is most familiar throughout the year.

7. *Adult Red Kite snatching up road-kill in Germany. This is just one of the food sources unwittingly provided by man that Kites are readily able to exploit* *(Robert Groß)*

8. *Juvenile Red Kite. Kites utilise several types of flight when foraging but slow circling or drifting low over the countryside is perhaps the most typical* *(Chris Gomersall)*

9. *Chicks only a few days old. Small chicks are covered with thick down, pure white on the head, but darker and with a sandy tint on the upperbody and wings* *(Tony Cross)*

10. *7-10 day old chick on a nest in central England. At this age, chicks are still covered with down and the first true feathers have yet to start showing* *(Ian Carter)*

11. *Adult with chick of about 2-2.5 weeks old. The first true feathers are now just beginning to show as dark, blood-filled shafts protruding from the wings* (Mike Read)

12. *Chick of about five weeks old. By this stage the body and wings are covered in brown feathers and only a trace of down remains on the head* (Mike Read)

13. *This poisoning incident, involving a Hare carcass laced with mevinphos, resulted in the death of at least three recently fledged Kites in central England in 2000 (Ian Carter)*

14. *Corvids such as this Carrion Crow are a frequent source of irritation to the Kite due to their aggressive mobbing behaviour*   *(Chris Gomersall)*

Chapter 11

MORTALITY AND SURVIVAL

The Kite's frequent association with human activities, together with its preference for animal carrion, make it highly vulnerable to deliberate persecution and accidental secondary poisoning resulting from pest control campaigns. This has led to the Kite's current patchy distribution in Europe. In areas where it is left unmolested, numbers are often high but, where persecution or secondary poisoning is intense, the species is likely to be rare or absent.

Although the Kite has few natural enemies when full-grown, nestlings are vulnerable to predation and, as with any wild bird, there are also losses through disease and starvation. In parts of the range, habitat alteration and changes in land management practices have had a detrimental effect on Kites. These threats are dealt with elsewhere in the book and this chapter concentrates on factors with the potential for more direct adverse impacts on Red Kite populations.

Human persecution

Illegal persecution, in several different forms, is still the main threat to Kites across much of the range. Kites are not always the specific targets of persecution and this is particularly the case with poison baits placed out in the open countryside. These are usually aimed at predators such as corvids and Foxes but they are completely indiscriminate and the Kite's supreme ability to detect animal carrion means that it suffers disproportionately. In some areas, despite their mainly scavenging lifestyle, Kites are viewed as a threat to game species or even livestock and here, direct persecution, including nest destruction, trapping and, particularly, shooting is the main threat.

Levels of persecution have been much reduced in central and northern Europe over recent decades and this has allowed populations, drastically reduced at the hands of man in the past, to recover. The reintroduction programme in Britain was only possible as a result of a reduction in persecution, although illegal killing is still far too frequent and has undoubtedly helped to reduce the rate of population increase and spread to new areas. In southern and eastern Europe, persecution remains as one of the most important factors affecting Kites and populations will only recover if this problem can be tackled effectively.

Even in areas where Kites are studied intensively, only a small proportion of dead birds are ever likely to be recovered so that the cause of death can be established. In England, it has been estimated, based on survival rates determined for individually marked birds, that only about one in five birds that die are found while still fresh enough to allow a full post-mortem to be carried out (Holmes *et al* 2000). The others are either found when badly decomposed or are not found at all. The proportion of birds not found is probably even higher when illegal killing is involved as, in these cases, it is in the interests of the individuals involved to conceal the evidence of their activities. When considering the figures given in the sections below it is therefore worth bearing in mind that reported incidents represent only the tip of the iceberg.

Illegal poisoning

This has been the major threat faced by the Red Kite during the last 150 years or more and one of the main factors that led to the complete loss of the species from parts of its range, including England and Scotland. It is a method of control that was once widely used by farmers and gamekeepers because it provided a cheap and easy way of destroying a whole range of predatory species. Baits, either animal carcasses or eggs, laced with poison and placed out in the open could account for several individuals with a minimum of effort, whereas shooting and trapping were more time consuming and often less effective. Since being outlawed in Britain, the use of poison baits has declined and pest species are now more often controlled by legal means such as shooting, snaring and the use of Larsen cage traps. Although only a small minority of individuals in Britain persist in the use of poison baits, it remains a completely indiscriminate form of control and birds of prey continue to be regular victims.

The Kite is particularly vulnerable to poisoning as it is such an efficient, opportunist scavenger and often gathers in numbers at a source of food. As a result, many individuals may be killed by a single bait. The recovery of the Welsh population has long been hindered by the use of poison baits to control corvids and Foxes, blamed by farmers for killing lambs. Between 1971 and 1989 a total of 24 Welsh Kites were found poisoned including five birds in one incident in 1989 (Lovegrove 1990). A more recent incident, in 1999, resulted in the death of only a single Kite but also at least one Buzzard, several Carrion Crows and no fewer than 19 Ravens (Peter Davis in litt). An analysis of the deaths of 119 Welsh Kites between 1950 and 1996 revealed that 29% were definitely poisoned and a further 12% were probably poisoned, together representing 62% of the birds for which it was possible to establish a likely cause of death (Cross & Davis 1998).

The reintroduced populations have also suffered and this is by far the most frequent cause of death for Kites in England. Since the start of the programme in 1989 a total of 20 birds have been found dead as a result of illegal poisoning and a further bird was poisoned but recovered and was released back into the wild (Carter & Grice 2000; Doug Simpson in litt). If anything, the problem is even greater in Scotland where, in 1997-2000 alone, at least 13 Kites were found illegally poisoned (Brian Etheridge pers comm.). It is thought that the Scottish incidents result mainly from routine poisoning campaigns carried out by gamekeepers managing moorland estates for Red Grouse. This is borne out by a strong correlation between confirmed bird of prey poisoning incidents and managed grouse moors in Scotland (RSPB Species Protection Database). There is an ongoing government-led campaign to reduce illegal poisoning in Britain and the Kite has played a useful role in helping to raise public awareness of this issue. In 1997, for example, a farmer in southern England was prosecuted and fined £4,000 for deliberately poisoning a Kite. The case received considerable local publicity and has hopefully deterred others from carrying out similar activities in the area.

In Spain, Villafuerte, Viñuela and Blanco (1998) showed that there was a strong correlation between areas with important populations of Rabbits (a valued game species) and recent declines in Kite numbers, and blamed this on persecution, particularly poisoning. Many hunters in Spain view large birds of prey as a threat to Rabbit populations and some openly admit to using illegal methods to control their numbers. Only in areas where game shooting is not important are Kite populations stable or increasing. The situation is thought to have worsened following recent reductions in Rabbit numbers as a result of Rabbit Haemorrhagic Disease. Some hunters have wrongly blamed the declines on predators and, as a result, persecution has increased. A similar situation existed in Spain in the 1950s when myxomatosis was responsible for significant reductions in Rabbit populations. During this period there was a government-sponsored campaign targeted at predators in order to try to preserve Rabbit numbers and it was estimated that as many as 10,000 Red and Black Kites were killed between 1954 and 1961 (Garzón 1974).

It is impossible to know how many Kites have been killed in more recent times in Spain as controlling birds of prey is now illegal and incidents are therefore not widely reported. However, Villafuerte, Viñuela and Blanco (1998) reported 91 recent cases where Kites were killed by humans, 77 of which involved the use of poisons. Hernández (1997) concluded that the Red Kite was the species worst affected by this problem in Spain and gave summary details of 150 birds poisoned in only 16 incidents. At least 17 of these birds had been ringed as chicks in Germany showing the potential for this threat to affect breeding populations in other areas. In parts of Spain, baits are also put out in order to try to kill Wolves and other mammalian predators blamed for taking livestock or gamebirds, and this adds to the risk that birds of prey will be poisoned.

Poisoning also affects Kites in parts of Europe where populations are still very low and the loss of even a small number of individuals is of great concern. In the Netherlands, for example, where there is only a handful of breeding pairs, 12 Kites were poisoned between 1976 and 1980, helping to prevent a more rapid recolonisation of the country (Cadbury 1991).

The type of poison favoured for use in baits varies from area to area depending on what is most readily available. The following list gives details of the most frequently abused poisons in Britain:

Fenthion: A discontinued organophosphorus veterinary product formerly used by farmers to control warble fly infestations of sheep and therefore widely available. This is the most commonly used illegal poison in Wales and has presumably been stockpiled by some for this purpose.

Mevinphos: A highly toxic organophosphorus insecticide formerly available under the trade name 'Phosdrin' but no longer approved for agricultural use. It has been stockpiled by some people for use in poison baits, and is by far the most common poison involved in Kite incidents in England.

Strychnine: Licensed for use underground to control Moles but also highly toxic to birds and frequently used illegally in poison baits.

Alphachloralose: A narcotic used as a bird stupefying agent and a rodenticide. The high concentration formula that has been used in illegal baits is only available under licence to pest controllers, although there is some evidence that it is also imported illegally from sources in the Republic of Ireland (RSPB Investigations Unit). Until recently this was the pesticide most frequently abused for wildlife poisoning in Britain.

Carbofuran: A highly toxic carbamate insecticide used when growing root crops, brassicas and cereals and therefore commercially available to farmers. The first recorded persecution incident was in 1988 but, in Scotland, it has become the pesticide most frequently recorded in wildlife poisoning incidents. Its approval for use has now been withdrawn.

Various other compounds, mainly agricultural pesticides, have been responsible for the death of Red Kites when used in poison baits. These include metaldehyde (found in slug pellets), diazinon, malathion, aldicarb, endrin and phorate. In Spain, carbofuran and fenthion are responsible for the majority of Kite poisoning incidents.

Shooting

It is almost impossible to assess the true impact of illegal shooting on Kite populations as birds shot and killed, or injured badly enough to be captured, will inevitably be concealed by the perpetrator. Only when the act of shooting is witnessed or if a bird is injured and later found and reported, do incidents come to light. As in the case of poisoning, the Kite is particularly vulnerable to this form of persecution as its nest and roost sites are easy to find and it often flies slowly, low over the ground in search of food, presenting a relatively easy target. Added to this, it is not particularly wary of humans and can often be found close to villages or farm buildings, offering more frequent opportunities for shooting than is the case with other, more elusive, birds of prey.

In England, since the start of the reintroduction programme, four birds have been found with shotgun injuries and a fifth bird was found dead with a lead pellet from a shotgun cartridge lodged in its neck. Of the four injured birds, three were successfully rehabilitated by vets at the Institute of Zoology (based at

London Zoo) and released back into the wild. The fourth failed to respond sufficiently well to treatment and had to be destroyed.

Shooting is also thought to be a significant problem in parts of Spain where a proportion of the country's many hunters view Kites as a threat to game and the species is blamed by some rural dwellers for taking chickens. Viñuela (1993) witnessed people shooting at Kite roosts when he was carrying out survey work but was well aware that the vast majority of incidents went undetected. In other southern European countries with large numbers of hunters but mainly low numbers of Kites, opportunist shooting is also likely to be a problem although good information is lacking.

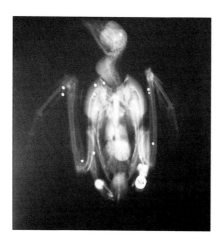

The numerous lead pellets from a shotgun cartridge are clearly visible in this x-ray of a wounded Kite in England (Institute of Zoology)

Egg collecting

Ever since British Red Kites were reduced to a small remnant population in central Wales in the early 1900s, their eggs have been highly sought after by collectors, and this is one of the factors that has prevented a more rapid recovery of the Welsh population. In the 1950s and '60s when the number of known nests was between 10 and 24, very few years went by without at least one nest being robbed and many incidents no doubt went undetected. In 1956, only three young were known to have fledged and yet at least four nests were robbed of their eggs, severely reducing breeding productivity in that year. In 1985 no fewer than 10 nests were robbed, affecting over one fifth of the total breeding population (Lovegrove 1990), and in most years during the 1990s, clutches have been taken.

Strenuous efforts have been made to protect nests from egg collectors, involving the use of sophisticated electronic equipment, as well as the more labour intensive 24-hour watches. Even the army has been drafted in to watch over nests thought to be particularly at risk. In some cases, where nests were known to be vulnerable, the decision has been taken to remove the eggs so that they could be hatched and reared safely in captivity. The adult birds were sometimes given Buzzard eggs so that they continued to sit and the artificially reared young were then replaced in a suitable Kite nest when about 10 days old. As with most other birds of prey, the adults readily accept this unlikely sequence of events, with eggs suddenly being replaced by well-grown chicks or an extra chick appearing in the nest, and over 50 young have now been reared in this way. As the Welsh population continues to increase, so the impact of a few lost clutches each year diminishes. Nevertheless, each nest that fails as a result of human interference inevitably slows the rate of population increase and spread to new areas.

The reintroduced populations have been little affected by egg-collecting, perhaps because collectors prefer to target the native population in Wales and also because, as Kite numbers have increased, there has been a corresponding reduction in the 'rarity value' of the eggs. Although some eggs will no doubt be taken as Kites spread to new areas (and there is evidence that at least one clutch has already been stolen from a nest in southern England) it is hoped that the impact of this outdated activity will be minimal in future.

Accidental secondary poisoning

Incidents where birds of prey are poisoned accidentally as a consequence of the legal use, or accidental misuse, of a product are of great concern as they are particularly difficult to prevent. The most dramatic example of this form of poisoning involved the complete elimination of Peregrines and Sparrowhawks from large parts of their range in Britain, and elsewhere, following the widespread use of organochlorine pesticides such as DDT, endrin and dieldrin. These were used as insecticides in the 1950s and '60s, often being coated onto grain before sowing, and, although they have a relatively low toxicity when compared to some other pesticides, they are extremely persistent in the environment and become concentrated in the bodies of predators at the top of the food chain. This led to widespread breeding failure of birds of prey through egg-shell thinning and also caused the direct mortality of adults. Despite the deliberate withholding of information by manufacturers and other vested interests on the effects of these pesticides, the case against them eventually became overwhelming and they were either banned or severely restricted in use, to be replaced by less persistent products. Peregrine and Sparrowhawk numbers recovered as a result and both species are now fully restored to their former status.

Hopefully lessons have been learnt from this episode and, in Britain, there are now monitoring schemes in place, such as MAFF's Wildlife Incident

Investigation Scheme (WIIS) in order to help identify potential problems with pesticides at an early stage. Post-mortems are carried out on dead mammals and birds reported to the scheme and, where poisoning is suspected, tissues are analysed for the presence of pesticides. The cause of death of many of the Kites referred to in the sections below was established as a result of dead birds being submitted to the WIIS scheme.

Agricultural pesticides

In the early 1960s, dieldrin, one of the organochlorines, was widely used in sheep dips in Wales. Kite breeding productivity was particularly poor during this period and it is possible that, through scavenging on sheep carcasses, birds were being adversely affected by secondary poisoning. This was shown to be the case with Golden Eagles in western Scotland (Lockie, Ratcliffe & Balharry 1969) but the evidence for a similar effect in Welsh Kites was not conclusive. Chemical analysis of unhatched eggs revealed only low levels of organochlorine residues and measurements of egg-shells showed a decline in thickness of only 4.5%, compared to more than 20% for raptor species subject to marked breeding failure as a result of contamination with organochlorines (Davis & Newton 1981). Dieldrin was withdrawn from use in sheep dips in 1965, thus removing the potential for adverse effects on Kites. Slight decreases in egg-shell thickness have also been found in central Europe as a result of organochlorine use as a seed dressing. Weber and Stubbe (1995) recorded average reductions of 4.3% in the 1950s and found that reductions were largest in areas where intensive agriculture dominated the landscape.

A small number of recent Kite poisoning incidents in Britain are thought to have involved the misuse of agricultural pesticides, resulting from a failure to follow the label instructions of a product, rather than a deliberate attempt to poison wildlife. An example of this type of incident is the spillage of pesticide-treated grain when it is approved for use only if drilled directly into the soil in order to make it inaccessible to birds. This may result in the death of grain feeders such as pigeons and, with highly toxic products, there is then the risk of secondary poisoning of predators or scavengers. In central England in the 2000 breeding season, a four-week old Kite nestling was found dead on the nest, together with a partly consumed Woodpigeon carcass containing pink-dyed maize seed. Analysis of the maize and tissues from the nestling revealed the presence of bendiocarb, a seed dressing, in both, and it was concluded that the Kite had been poisoned. A subsequent investigation by staff from the Farming and Rural Conservation Agency failed to find out how the maize had become available to the Woodpigeon but it is likely that, through carelessness, some had been spilled onto the ground.

Where there is strong evidence that a pesticide has been misused, leading to the death of non-target wildlife species, MAFF have the powers to prosecute those responsible.

Rodenticides

The Red Kite has helped to highlight some potentially serious problems with the highly toxic second-generation anticoagulant rodenticides that are now used widely across Europe. Although these products are sold under a variety of different trade names they are all based on a few different active ingredients, namely difenacoum, bromadiolone, brodifacoum and flocoumafen. They are effective in areas where Rats have developed resistance to first generation poisons such as warfarin and can kill with only a single feed, whereas warfarin requires several feeds in order to be effective. The problem for wildlife stems from the fact that these compounds are several hundred times more toxic than warfarin, and so there is a far greater risk of secondary poisoning when predators or scavengers feed on poisoned rodents. Second-generation rodenticides also have relatively long biological half-lives and are slow to break down once they have been incorporated into the tissues of an animal. There is therefore a danger that a damaging level of rodenticide may build up by repeated ingestion of relatively small doses in poisoned prey.

Although problems with secondary rodenticide poisoning have been reported for several species in Britain, most notably the Barn Owl (Newton *et al* 1999) and Polecat (Shore *et al* 1996), there are certain aspects of the Red Kite's ecology that make it particularly vulnerable to this threat. This is because (i) in some areas Rats form a major part of the diet throughout the year, (ii) the Kite's scavenging lifestyle means that most Rats are taken as carrion, where there is a greater chance of contamination by rodenticides and (iii) Kites are generally not wary of people and often forage around farm buildings, where rodent control is frequently carried out (Carter & Burn 2000).

In 1998 and 1999, tissue samples from eight dead Kites in England were found to contain residues of second-generation rodenticides. Post-mortems carried out on three of these birds revealed internal bleeding, strongly suggesting that the anticoagulant effect of the poison was the cause of death. In the other five cases the significance of the residue levels found was not clear and it was not possible to establish the cause of death. In 1999 and 2000, six nestlings from three different nests in northern Scotland were found dead on or close to the nest. Post-mortems revealed internal bleeding and residues of bromadiolone or difenacoum were found in the liver of each bird showing that they had been poisoned (Brian Etheridge in litt).

Recent studies carried out by the Centre for Ecology and Hydrology (at Monks Wood) and the Scottish Agricultural Science Agency found that 65% of 29 liver samples, from birds that had died from a variety of different causes in England and Scotland, contained rodenticide residues, although not all at levels thought likely to have caused detrimental effects (Shore *et al* 2000; Sharp & Hunter 1999). This is a far higher proportion than is the case in Barn Owls, for example, where the figure is about 35% for dead birds tested in recent years (Newton *et al* 1999). Such a widespread level of contamination is of great concern, particularly as the residues were often above the levels found in Barn Owls known to have died as a result of rodenticide poisoning.

On the Continent, second-generation rodenticides are used to reduce agricultural damage caused by vole plagues and this has led to mass mortalities of birds of prey as a result of secondary poisoning. In Switzerland, for example, an incident in the early 1980s involving the use of bromadiolone to control Water Voles (an agricultural pest in parts of Europe!) led to the deaths of no fewer than 25 Red Kites as well as other raptor species (Beguin 1983). More recently, the use of bromadiolone to control voles has led to the deaths of many Red Kites in France and Spain. This problem has been implicated in substantial local declines in the breeding population in parts of France, as well as affecting wintering birds from central Europe (Ligue pour la Protection des Oiseaux in litt; Viñuela, Martí & Ruiz 1999). There have been very few incidents in central Wales where the mainly pastoral landscape is less well suited to Rats and they are not common in the diet (Davis & Davis 1981).

This is a very difficult issue to resolve as Rats in Britain and vole plagues on the Continent clearly need to be controlled and the use of anticoagulant rodenticides is usually the most effective method. In Britain the problem shows no signs of improving as Rats have benefited from the lack of severe winters in recent years and, in a few areas, have even developed resistance to some of the second-generation poisons. Although there are strict controls on the way that rodenticides can be used, such as the requirement for bait to be placed within a secure container, it is difficult to prevent some animals dying out in the open where they then become accessible to scavengers. This is also the case with the most toxic products, containing brodifacoum or flocoumafen, which are only approved for use within buildings. The use of vitamin K in animal feeds is a further cause for concern as such feeds have the potential to act as an antidote to anticoagulant rodenticides. Rats that gain access to feeds not only benefit from an artificial source of food but may then require a higher dose of poison to kill them, presenting a greater risk of secondary poisoning.

In many areas, the less toxic, first-generation rodenticides such as warfarin are still effective and can be used with relatively little risk of secondary poisoning. Where the more toxic products are used, it is essential that frequent searches for rodent carcasses are carried out, as required by the product label instructions, and any carcasses found must be disposed of safely by burning or burying rather than thrown onto an open dump, where they are accessible to scavengers.

Lead poisoning

Birds become vulnerable to lead poisoning, either by ingesting lead directly, as in the well-known example of the Mute Swan, adversely affected by lead fishing weights, or by feeding on prey species killed or injured by lead from shotgun cartridges. Marsh Harriers in southern France have been lethally poisoned by feeding on shot wildfowl, including scavenging on birds killed outright and taking live prey containing lead pellets as a result of a non-lethal injury (Pain *et al* 1993). Although lead ingested by a bird of prey is subsequently regurgitated, along with other indigestible material from prey, during the time it is in the acidic stomach it gradually dissolves, releasing the highly toxic lead into the blood-stream (Pain, Sears & Newton 1995). If this happens repeatedly, as is likely in an area where shooting is frequent, lead levels may build up until they begin to have adverse effects on the bird.

Analysis of regurgitated Kite pellets in England and Scotland has shown that lead from shotgun cartridges is, at times, ingested, although it occurs in only a very low proportion of pellets (Wildman, O'Toole & Summers 1998; Carter & Clarke in prep). The same has been found in southern Spain where the proportion of pellets containing lead was much lower than in Marsh Harriers and it was concluded that lead poisoning was unlikely to be a serious problem (Viñuela, Martí & Ruiz 1999). In Britain, the most likely source of lead is through scavenging on gamebirds or pest species such as Woodpigeons, Crows or Rabbits killed with a shotgun. All these species are common in the diet and so there is a risk that sufficient lead could be ingested to cause a problem. Wildfowl might also present a problem in Wales and Scotland as, in these countries, unlike in England, shotgun cartridges containing lead can still be used legally for shooting over wetland sites.

Lead in rifle-shot animals can also result in poisoning, as lead bullet fragments may remain lodged in the flesh to be swallowed by scavengers if the carcass is not retrieved. This was one of the main factors that caused the endangered California Condor to decline and is now hindering efforts to reintroduce it (Meretsky *et al* 1999). Farmers and gamekeepers in Britain control Rabbits by shooting them with a rifle, often at night when they are illuminated with high-powered lamps. The carcasses are frequently left where they fall, either because they are thought to reduce the likelihood of Fox predation of livestock or gamebirds, or simply because they have little value and it is time consuming to retrieve them.

Samples of liver tissue from 20 Kites found dead in England between 1994 and 1999 were analysed for lead by the Centre for Ecology and Hydrology (Shore *et al* 2000). Eleven of the 20 birds were found to have detectable lead residues, but only one bird had a residue noticeably higher than the usual background levels. This bird had been shot and, as all attempts at rehabilitation failed, it eventually had to be destroyed. Lead leaching from pellets lodged within its tissues may well have been an important factor in preventing its recovery. The only other case of lead poisoning of a Kite in Britain, involved a nestling collected from the southern England population in 2000 and taken to the Yorkshire release site. During its time in captivity it failed to develop at the same rate as the other birds in the pens and was subsequently taken to the Institute of Zoology for diagnosis. Analysis of a blood sample showed that lead levels were very high and, despite treatment, lead poisoning eventually resulted in death (Andrew Cunningham pers comm.). The source of the lead is not known for certain, but it is likely that food brought to the nest site by one of the adults was contaminated. If this bird had been left in the wild it would almost certainly have died on the nest and the incident would have gone unrecorded. Birds held in captivity, before release, are now fed mainly on carcasses killed by a rifle shot to the head and the head is then discarded to reduce the chance of contamination with lead bullet fragments. Rabbits shot through the body are closely examined to ensure that the bullet has passed completely through.

Electrocution and collision with powerlines

Mortality associated with powerlines has been reported for a wide range of species in various parts of the world. As a general rule, it is the heavier species with a high wing-loading, and therefore lower manoeuvrability, such as wildfowl and bustards, that are most vulnerable to collisions, whereas species with a large wing-span that habitually perch on the wire-supporting poles are at greater risk of electrocution (Janss 2000). Wing-span is important because, for a bird to be electrocuted, it must simultaneously touch either two separate wires or a wire and an earthed metal cross-support, for example, as it perches on the support. If only a single wire is touched then the electricity does not pass through the body of the bird and many species habitually perch on live wires with no ill effects.

The Kite, with its generally leisurely flight and superb eyesight, but large wing-span and long tail, seems more likely to be at risk of electrocution than collision and this is borne out by Janss's study of bird mortality associated with powerlines in southwest Spain. The study involved walking under lengths of powerline and recording the numbers of birds found dead from these two main causes. Electrocuted birds could be identified as they were mainly found directly under poles and showed burn marks to the wings, talons or beak. Table 16 shows the number of individuals killed by electrocution and collision for the species detected most often, together with an index of local abundance based on road transect counts, so that the relative threat from each cause of death can be assessed. Two different study areas were used, one containing powerlines thought to pose a high risk of collisions and the other with wires presenting a high risk of electrocution.

No Red or Black Kites were recorded as collision victims but both species were regular victims of electrocution. Nevertheless, the figures show that other species, in particular Common Buzzard and Raven, were far more vulnerable to this threat, with many more of each found electrocuted, despite their lower abundance in the study area. This is likely to be a reflection of their greater tendency to perch on the supporting poles than is the case with the two more aerial kite species.

Table 16: **Casualties of electrocution and collision found under powerlines in southwest Spain, 1991-93 (from Janss 2000)**

Species	Deaths from electrocution	Local index	Deaths from collision	Local index
White Stork	36	648	5	42
Black Kite	46	631	0	26
Red Kite	45	446	0	61
Griffon Vulture	5	1060	1	283
Common Buzzard	167	195	0	37
Great Bustard	0	0	16	7
Little Bustard	0	0	10	0
Raven	117	38	0	42

Information from other studies of raptors around the world suggests that the threat from collision with powerlines has often been exaggerated and many birds reported as collision victims are now thought more likely to have been killed by electrocution (Bevanger & Overskaug 1998). This supports a reassessment of the threat posed by powerlines in Britain as it has previously been assumed by some authors that birds found dead below wires had been killed mainly by flying into them rather than by electrocution. There is now conclusive evidence that Kites can be electrocuted by the standard, three wire, electricity powerlines that are widespread across Britain. There have been at least four birds killed in this way in Scotland and three in England, all of which were found dead with scorch marks visible on their wings or feet. These birds were found mainly below poles with transformer boxes where the complex arrangement of wires, together with the fact that such poles are more likely to be earthed, makes electrocution more likely.

In England, a further 10 birds have been found dead under powerlines in recent years having died from unknown causes. It is likely that at least some of these were also victims of electrocution.

There are various means of reducing the risk posed by powerlines and these have been adopted with considerable success in areas where problems have been most apparent. Coloured plastic balls or wire spirals may be attached to wires to make them more visible to birds. This has been done on powerlines close to important wetland reserves in Britain, such as the Ouse Washes in Norfolk, and has been successful in reducing the number of wildfowl killed by collision. The risk of electrocution can be reduced either by insulating dangerous sections of wire, for example by covering them with a length of plastic tube, or, by providing artificial perches well above the wires so that raptors do not attempt to perch on the metal cross supports. If Kites are found to be increasingly regular victims of electrocution as populations increase in Britain then these types of solution will be worth serious consideration in order to limit the number of birds killed.

Collision with vehicles

A small number of Kites in Britain have been found dead or injured at the edge of a road, having collided with passing traffic. This presumably occurs when a bird is feeding at a road-kill carcass but does not manage to fly up in time as a vehicle approaches at speed. On the few occasions when Kites in central England have been observed feeding on road-kills they have been very reluctant to land, preferring to fly in ever-tighter circles before swooping down, grabbing the carcass, and carrying it away to a more secure feeding site. Large carcasses are too heavy to lift but the Kite's wariness about landing in an unfamiliar situation means that it remains constantly alert to potential danger and, in most cases, seems unlikely to be caught by surprise by an approaching vehicle.

This behaviour differs significantly from that of species like the Barn Owl, known to suffer high mortality from collisions with vehicles (Shawyer 1998). Barn Owls hunt by quartering low over the ground and birds may inadvertently fly into the path of an oncoming vehicle or, as a result of their lightweight bodies, get caught in the slipstream of high-sided vehicles. In the western United States, migrant Rough-legged Buzzards are regular victims of traffic and it is thought that their carrion-feeding habits, together with their lack of familiarity with roads through breeding in remote parts of the Arctic, make them particularly vulnerable (Newton 1979). Kites, like the Crows and Rooks which also exploit road-kills as a source of food, are perhaps mainly at serious risk from collisions when recently fledged and inexperienced, or if not fully fit. The Kite's relatively low level of vulnerability to this threat is shown well by information on road mortalities of raptors and owls in Spain (Muntaner & Mayol 1996). Up to 1992, a total of 18 Red Kites had been found dead on roads during survey work, compared with 62 Buzzards, 749 Barn Owls and no less than 941 Little Owls. The particularly high figures for Barn and Little Owl partly reflect their large populations in Spain but, even when expressed as a proportion of relative population size, are far higher than the figure for Red Kite, showing that they are more vulnerable than the Kite to this cause of death.

Red Kites are relatively infrequent victims of collision with road traffic. This is a far more important mortality factor for species such as the Little Owl (above) and Barn Owl

(Ian Carter)

It is not only collision with road traffic that results in this type of traumatic death. Trains have been involved in at least two incidents in Scotland (Brian Etheridge pers comm.) and another in England, where a wandering bird from Wales was killed. Aircraft have been involved in at least two incidents, including an adult in central England, killed by a light aircraft taking off from a small airfield close to the bird's nest site. The pilot realised that he had collided with a bird as his plane took off and the fatally injured Kite was found during a subsequent search of the runway. In Wales, the cockpit window of a military jet was smashed as a result of a collision with a Kite, the bird being identified from feathers found inside the cockpit (Tony Cross pers comm.).

Other human factors

The trapping of birds of prey was formerly widespread in Britain and probably played an important role in the past decline of the Kite and other species. Larsen cage traps are now used as a legal means of controlling Crows and Magpies by exploiting the territorial behaviour of these species during the breeding season. A live 'call-bird' is placed in one compartment and when other birds of the same species arrive to chase it out of their territory they are caught in an adjacent compartment. Occasionally, gamekeepers have found Kites caught in these traps, particularly when they are baited with carrion in order to trap the first 'call-bird'. This should not pose a serious threat to Kites as it is a legal requirement to check such traps at least once each day and any non-target birds caught accidentally can then be released.

Kites occasionally become tangled up in refuse, either when foraging on rubbish dumps or, with nestlings, as a result of material brought to the nest as decoration by the adults. One chick, taken from a southern England nest for release in central England, was found to have plastic wrapped so tightly around its leg that it had begun to cut into the flesh. It recovered fully following treatment but would not have been so lucky if the nest had not been visited and it had been left to fend for itself in the wild. Another chick, this time in northern Scotland, was found to have crawled inside a plastic bag in the nest when only 2-3 days old. It was freed and the plastic bag, together with other rubbish, removed from the nest. Once again, this chick probably only survived as a result of a timely visit to the nest site (Brian Etheridge pers comm.). These incidents are, thankfully, rare and apart from trying to reduce the amount of litter that ends up in our country-side, there is little that can be done to prevent them from occurring.

Natural mortality factors

Full-grown, healthy Kites have no serious predators other than man, although they are no doubt very occasionally killed by large raptors such as the larger species of eagle, Goshawk and Eagle Owl, or as a result of unusually intense skirmishes with Buzzards, Ravens or rival Kites. The nestlings are much more vulnerable and are taken by a range of opportunist avian and mammalian predators, especially if they are left unguarded by the parent birds. Corvids such as Carrion Crows, Jackdaws and Magpies are suspected of killing small young from time to time and will take eggs if they get the opportunity. Grey Squirrels are also potential predators of small chicks and eggs, and, in Scotland, Pine Martens have been blamed for a small number of nest failures.

In Wales, Ravens and Kites have a very uneasy relationship in the breeding season and a Kite nest sited close to an active Raven nest rarely results in the young fledging successfully (Davis & Newton 1981). The main problem comes when the Raven young fledge which often occurs while the Kite chicks are still small. If they stray too close to the Kite nest then the adults of both species become involved, each fearing for the safety of their own young. In one extreme case, investigated by Tony Cross, an adult Kite was killed following direct aggression from one of the adult Ravens. When the Welsh population was still small and vulnerable, preventative measures were taken to avoid conflict between Kites and the far more numerous Ravens. This involved removing eggs from Raven nests, under licence, if a Kite pair was nesting nearby, and placing them in alternative Raven nests to be reared by surrogate parents well out of harm's way. On the other side of the Atlantic, Ravens have been responsible for the direct predation of California Condor eggs and in order to protect such a highly endangered species, conservationists have resorted to shooting Ravens nesting in the same area as Condors (Snyder & Snyder 2000).

Various diseases have been recorded in both adult and nestling Kites in Britain. Infections caused by *Salmonella* and *Escherichia coli* bacteria have been found in Welsh chicks, perhaps not surprisingly, considering the putrefying meat that is sometimes brought to nests. It is not known to what extent Kites are resistant to such bacteria as might be expected in a species that thrives on carrion, and it is perhaps only small nestlings that are usually affected. Fully grown birds found dead in Britain have been diagnosed with diseases such as aspergillosis (a fungal infection), avian tuberculosis, avian pox (a skin disease) and trichomoniasis, and there are no doubt others that have yet to be recorded. Whether these infections regularly cause the death of otherwise healthy birds or affect mainly individuals already in poor condition for another reason is not known. When assessing the threats faced by a wild bird species, disease is usually a long way down the list of factors considered and is rarely thought to be a significant cause of population decline. However, it is now believed that disease is the most likely cause of recent dramatic declines and even local extinctions in several species of Gyps vulture in

India (Andrew Cunningham pers comm.), showing that, at least on rare occasions, population level effects do occur.

The extent of losses resulting from natural causes is extremely difficult to quantify in wild birds, particularly in full-grown individuals, as, when birds feel unwell, they generally seek seclusion and cover, where they are less vulnerable to predators. The carcasses are therefore less likely to be found than is the case when birds are killed quickly by poisons or as a result of electrocution, for example. Even when a carcass is recovered, the cause of death may still be difficult to determine, particularly if, as is often the case, several different factors are involved. Consider, for example, a bird that contracts a disease and becomes gradually weaker until its ability to find food is restricted and it is at risk of starving to death. If food in the area is abundant and weather conditions are good then it has a chance of surviving until the worst effects of the disease have passed. If, however, the weather deteriorates, making foraging difficult, and the local food supply is poor, then it is much less likely to survive. In this case, the eventual death of the bird is the result of a combination of different factors that would be impossible to fully disentangle by a post-mortem examination.

Natural mortality factors can also be masked if the means by which a bird finally dies is related to human activities. A bird weakened by disease or hunger may be more likely to scavenge around farm buildings where it is at greater risk of secondary rodenticide poisoning, or it may be more sluggish when flying up from a road carcass and so end up colliding with a vehicle. A weakened bird is also more vulnerable to predation, particularly if it becomes so weak that it is unable to fly. Such complex interactions should always be taken into account when trying to assess the significance of different mortality factors in a species.

Life expectancy and survival rates

Kites have the potential to be very long-lived and it is a sad fact that, across much of their range, death is likely to come prematurely at the hands of man. The oldest Welsh Kite so far recorded was ringed 24 years before it died and there have been several other birds that have approached 20 years of age (Cross & Davis 1998). There are similar records from other parts of Europe, including a German bird found almost 26 years after it was first ringed. In captivity, where there is no risk of premature death as a result of persecution, and a regular food supply is guaranteed, there is a record of a Red Kite living for at least 38 years (Newton 1979).

Studies of individually marked wing-tagged birds in Wales and young birds fitted with both wing-tags and radio-transmitters before release in England and Scotland have provided very good information on annual survival rates. As with all species, young, and therefore inexperienced, birds are more vulnerable than adults and this is reflected in lower survival rates. Combining the figures for released and wild-fledged birds in England in 1989-94, a minimum of 80% of birds survived their first year, rising to 94% in the second year and 95% for birds in their third year or older. In Scotland survival rates were somewhat lower at 50% for first-year birds, rising to 88% for birds in their third year or older (Evans *et al* 1999).

In both areas the lower survival rates for first-year birds relates not only to their lack of experience compared to adults but also to differences in behaviour. First-year birds often disperse away from the release site, leaving an area where local people are familiar with the species and levels of persecution are usually low. They may wander into areas where persecution is more common and so a higher proportion of these birds are likely to be killed. In contrast, adults are generally sedentary, and by remaining in the core breeding area, are less likely to fall victim to persecution. In order to calculate more realistic survival rates for first-year birds that do not disperse, released birds that remained in central England during their first winter, between the two main dispersal periods of autumn and spring, were considered (Carter & Grice 2000). In all, this involved 43 individuals and, amazingly, all 43 survived the six-month period from October to March. Whilst this shows just how well suited Kites are to the local countryside, these figures would not be realistic for a well-established population. As with any species, increasing population density will lead to greater competition for food and therefore lower survival rates.

Survival rates in Wales have been estimated from re-sightings of wing-tagged birds as at least 60% for first-year birds, rising to 95% for territorial adults (Newton, Davis & Davis 1989), not dissimilar to the figures for birds rein-troduced into more suitable lowland areas. The more rapid increase in the reintroduced populations is mainly the result of far higher levels of breeding productivity and a reduced average age of first breeding, rather than significant differences in survival rates of full-grown birds.

SCIENTIFIC NAMES

Birds

American Black Vulture *Coragyps atratus*
Barn Owl *Tyto alba*
Bearded Vulture (Lammergeier) *Gypaetus barbatus*
Blackbird *Turdus merula*
Black-headed Gull *Larus ridibundus*
Black Kite *Milvus migrans*
Black-shouldered Kite *Elanus caeruleus*
Black Vulture *Aegypius monachus*
Booted Eagle *Hieraaetus pennatus*
Bullfinch *Pyrrhula pyrrhula*
(Common) Buzzard *Buteo buteo*
California Condor *Gymnogyps californianus*
Carrion Crow *Corvus corone*
Cattle Egret *Bubulcus ibis*
Chicken (Domestic Fowl) *Gallus* spp.
Cliff Swallow *Petrochelidon pyrrhonota*
Coot *Fulica atra*
Curlew *Numenius arquata*
Domestic/Feral Pigeon *Columba livia*
Eagle Owl *Bubo bubo*
Fulmar *Fulmarus glacialis*
Golden Eagle *Aquila chrysaetos*
Goshawk *Accipiter gentilis*
Great Bustard *Otis tarda*
Grey Partridge *Perdix perdix*
Griffon Vulture *Gyps fulvus*
Gyr Falcon *Falco rusticolus*
Hen Harrier *Circus cyaneus*
(Grey) Heron *Ardea cinerea*
Hobby *Falco subbuteo*
Imperial Eagle *Aquila adalberti*
Jackdaw *Corvus monedula*
Jay *Garrulus glandarius*
(Common) Kestrel *Falco tinnunculus*
Lanner Falcon *Falco biarmicus*
Lesser Black-backed Gull *Larus fuscus*

Lesser Kestrel *Falco naumanni*
Little Bustard *Tetrax tetrax*
Little Owl *Athene noctua*
Magpie *Pica pica*
Mallard *Anas platyrhynchos*
Marsh Harrier *Circus aeruginosus*
Mississippi Kite *Ictinia mississippiensis*
Montagu's Harrier *Circus pygargus*
Moorhen *Gallinula chloropus*
Mute Swan *Cygnus olor*
Osprey *Pandion haliaetus*
Peregrine *Falco peregrinus*
(Common) Pheasant *Phasianus colchicus*
Raven *Corvus corax*
Red Grouse *Lagopus lagopus*
Red-legged Partridge *Alectoris rufa*
Robin *Erithacus rubecula*
Rook *Corvus frugilegus*
Rough-legged Buzzard *Buteo lagopus*
Skylark *Alauda arvensis*
Snail Kite *Rostrhamus sociabilis*
Song Thrush *Turdus philomelos*
Sparrowhawk *Accipiter nisus*
Starling *Sturnus vulgaris*
Turkey Vulture *Cathartes aura*
White Stork *Ciconia ciconia*
White-tailed Kite *Elanus leucurus*
White-tailed Eagle *Haliaeetus albicilla*
Woodpecker *Picus/Dendrocopos* spp.
Woodpigeon *Columba palumbus*

Mammals
Badger *Meles meles*
Common Vole *Microtus arvalis*
Fallow Deer *Dama dama*
Field Vole *Microtus agrestis*
Fox *Vulpes vulpes*
Grey Squirrel *Sciurus carolinensis*
(Common) Hamster *Cricetus cricetus*

(Brown) Hare *Lepus capensis*
Hedgehog *Erinaceus europaeus*
Mink *Mustela vison*
Mole *Talpa europaea*
Muntjac Deer *Muntiacus reevesi*
Pine Marten *Martes martes*
Polecat *Mustela putorius*
Rabbit *Oryctolagus cuniculus*
(Common) Rat *Rattus norvegicus*
Red Squirrel *Sciurus vulgaris*
Roe Deer *Capreolus capreolus*
Stoat *Mustela erminea*
Water Vole *Arvicola terrestris*
Weasel *Mustela nivalis*
Wild Boar *Sus scrofa*
Wolf *Canis lupus*
Woodmouse *Apodemus sylvaticus*

Reptiles and amphibians
Common Frog *Rana temporaria*

Fish
Brown Trout *Salmo trutta*
Tench *Tinca tinca*

Plants
Ash *Fraxinus excelsior*
Beech *Fagus sylvatica*
English Oak *Quercus robur*
Field Maple *Acer campestre*
Larch *Larix* spp.
Norway Spruce *Picea abies*
Poplar *Populus* spp.
Scots Pine *Pinus sylvestris*
Sessile Oak *Quercus petraea*
Sycamore *Acer pseudoplatanus*
Turkey Oak *Quercus cerris*

BIBLIOGRAPHY

Adamski, A. 1995. Status, distribution and numbers of the Red Kite *Milvus milvus* in Poland. *Vogel und Umwelt* 8: 21-29.

Allavena, S., Fabbrizzi, F., Cecchi, R. & Galgano, R. 1996. Reintroduction of the Red Kite *Milvus milvus* in Tuscany, Italy. In Pandolfi, M (ed.) *Abstracts of the 2nd International Conference on Raptors*, 65. Urbino, Italy.

Anon. 1996. European News. *British Birds* 89: 25-45.

Baker, K. 1993. *Identification Guide to European Non-Passerines: BTO Guide 24.* BTO, Thetford.

Beguin, J. 1983. *Report on the chemical control of voles.* The Department of Agriculture of the Republic and Canton of Neuchatel, Neuchatel.

Bergier, P. 1987. Les rapaces diurnes du Maroc. *Annales du CEEP, 3.* Aix en Provence.

Bevanger, K. & Overskaug, K. 1998. Utility structures as a mortality factor for raptors and owls in Norway. In Chancellor, R.D., Meyburg, B.-U. & Ferrero, J.J. (eds.) *Holarctic Birds of Prey: Proceedings of an International Conference*, 381-392. ADENEX/WWGBP, Calamonte, Spain.

Bijlsma, R.G. 1997. Buzzard *Buteo buteo* (species account). In Hagemeijer, W.J.M. & Blair, M.J. (eds.) *The EBCC Atlas of European Breeding Birds: Their distribution and abundance.* Poyser, London.

Blanco, J.C. 1982. *Ecología trófica invernal del Milano Real* Milvus milvus *en Doñana.* Tesis de Licenciatura. Universidad de Oviedo.

Blanco, J.C. & González, J.L. 1992. *El Libro Rojo de los Vertebrados de España.* ICONA, Madrid.

Blanco, J.C., González, J.L. & Hiraldo, F. 1990. Trophic and spatial relationships between wintering Red Kites *Milvus milvus* and Marsh Harriers *Circus aeruginosus* in the Guadalquivir marshes. *J. Misc. Zool.* 14: 161-166.

Blanco, J.C., Hiraldo, F. & Heredia, B. 1990. Variations in the diet and foraging behaviour of a wintering Red Kite *Milvus milvus* population in response to changes in food availability. *Ardeola* 37: 267-278.

Brown, L. 1970. *Eagles.* Arthur Barker, London.

Bustamante, J. 1993. Post-fledging dependence period and development of flight and hunting behaviour in the Red Kite *Milvus milvus. Bird Study* 40: 181-188.

Bustamante, J. & Hiraldo, F. 1993. The function of aggressive chases by breeding Black and Red Kites *Milvus migrans* and *M. milvus* during the post-fledging dependence period. *Ibis* 135: 139-147.

Cadbury, J. 1991. *Persecution: birds of prey and owls killed in the UK, 1979-1989.* RSPB/Nature Conservancy Council.

Cade, T.J. 2000. Progress in translocation of diurnal raptors. In Chancellor, R.D. & Meyburg, B.-U. (eds.) *Raptors at Risk: Proceedings of the V World Conference on Birds of Prey and Owls*, 343-372. WWGBP, Berlin.

Campbell, B. & Lack, E. (eds.). 1985. *A Dictionary of Birds*. Poyser, Calton.

Carter, I. 1998. The changing fortunes of the Red Kite in Suffolk. *Suffolk Birds* 46: 6-10.

Carter, I. & Burn, A. 2000. Problems with rodenticides: The threat to Red Kites and other wildlife. *British Wildlife* 11: 192-197.

Carter, I., Evans, I. & Crockford, N. 1995. The Red Kite Re-introduction Project in Britain – progress so far and future plans. *British Wildlife* 7: 18-25.

Carter, I. & Grice, P. 2000. Studies of re-established Red Kites in England. *British Birds* 93: 304-322.

Carter, I., McQuaid, M., Snell, N. & Stevens, P. 1999. The Red Kite *Milvus milvus* Reintroduction Project: Modelling the impact of translocating Kite young within England. *J. Raptor Res.* 33: 251-254.

Clark, J.M. & Eyre, J.A. (eds.). 1993. *Birds of Hampshire*. Hampshire Ornithological Society.

Clarke, R. 1996. *Montagu's Harrier*. Arlequin Press, Chelmsford.

Collar, N.J. & Andrew, A. 1988. *Birds to watch: the ICBP world check-list of threatened birds*. ICBP Technical Publication 8, Cambridge.

Conzemius, T. 1998. Revierkartierung der 'Territorialen Saison-Population' des Rotmilans *Milvus milvus* 1997 in Luxembourg. *Regulus Wiss. Ber* 17: 1-26.

Cordero, P.J., Evans, I.M., Parkin, D.T. & Galbraith, C.A. 1997. Studies of the genetics of a naturalised population of Red Kites *Milvus milvus* in England established by translocation. In Tew, T.E., Crawford, T.J., Spencer, J.W., Stevens, D.P., Usher, M.B. & Warren, J. (eds.) *The role of genetics in conserving small populations*, 89-96. JNCC, Peterborough.

Corso, A. Palumbo, G., Manzi, A., Salerno, M., Sanna, M. & Carafa, M. 1999. Risultati preliminary dell'indagine nazionale sul nibbio reale *Milvus milvus* svernante in Italia. *Avocetta* 23: 12-.

Cramp, S. & Simmons, K.E.L. (eds.) 1980. *The Birds of the Western Palearctic,* Vol. II. Oxford University Press.

Cross, A.V. & Davis, P.E. 1998. *The Red Kite of Wales*. The Welsh Kite Trust, Llandrindod Wells.

D'Arcy, G. 1999. *Ireland's Lost Birds*. Four Court's Press, Dublin

Davis, P. 1993. The Red Kite in Wales: setting the record straight. *British Birds* 86: 295-298.

Davis, P.E. & Davis, J.E. 1981. The food of the Red Kite in Wales. *Bird Study* 28: 33-44.

Davis, P.E. & Newton, I. 1981. Population and breeding of Red Kites in Wales over a 30-year period. *J. Animal Ecol.* 50: 759-772.

Delibes, M. & García, L. 1984. Hábitos alimenticios del Milano Real en Doñana durante el periodo de cria. *Ardeola* 31: 115-121.

Encalado, J.J.R. 1998. Red Kites 'playing' with newspaper. *British Birds* 91: 233-234.

Evans, I.M., Cordero, P.J. & Parkin, D.T. 1998. Successful breeding at one year of age by Red Kites *Milvus milvus* in southern England. *Ibis* 140: 53-57.

Evans, I.M., Dennis, R.H., Orr-Ewing, D.C., Kjellén, N., Andersson, P-O., Sylvén, M., Senosiain, A. & Carbo, F.C. 1997. The re-establishment of Red Kite breeding populations in Scotland and England. *British Birds* 90: 123-138.

Evans, I.M. & Pienkowski, M.W. 1991. World status of the Red Kite: A background to the experimental reintroduction to England and Scotland. *British Birds* 84: 171-187.

Evans, I.M., Summers, R.W., O'Toole, L., Orr-Ewing, D.C., Evans, R., Snell, N. & Smith, J. 1999. Evaluating the success of translocating Red Kites *Milvus milvus* to the UK. *Bird Study* 46: 129-144.

Fisher, J. 1947. *Natural history of the Kite.* RSPB Annual Report, 1947.

Forsman, D. 1999. *The Raptors of Europe and the Middle East: A Handbook of Field Identification.* Poyser, London.

Gamauf, A. 1995. Schwarzmilan und Rotmilan in Österreich: Populationsentwicklung und verbreitung. In Müller, F. (ed.) *Rotmilan* Milvus milvus, 29-38. Vogel und Umwelt. (In German with English summary).

García, J.T., Viñuela, J. & Sunyer, C. 1998. Geographic variation of the winter diet of the Red Kite *Milvus milvus* in the Iberian Peninsula. *Ibis* 140: 302-309.

Garzón, J. 1974. Contribución al estudio del estatus, alimentación y protección de las Falconiformes en España central. *Ardeola* 19: 279-330.

George, K. 1994. Zur Überwinterung des Rotmilans *Milvus milvus* im nördlichen Harzvorland (Sachsen-Anhalt). *Vogelwelt* 115: 127-132.

George, K. 1995. Überwinterung von Rotmilanen *Milvus milvus* im nördlichen Harzvorland/Sachsen-Anhalt. In Müller, F. (ed.) *Rotmilan* Milvus milvus. Vogel und Umwelt, 59-66 (In German with English summary).

Glutz Von Blotzheim, U., Bauer, K.M. & Bezzel, E. 1971. *Handbuch der Vögel Mitteleuropas.* Frankfurt-am-Main, Vol. 4.

Gómez-Tejedor, H. 1998. Comportamiento cleptoparásito del Milano Real *Milvus milvus* en un vertedero. In Chancellor, R.D., Meyburg, B.-U. & Ferrero, J.J. (eds.) *Holarctic Birds of Prey: Proceedings of an International Conference,* 173-176. ADENEX/WWGBP, Calamonte, Spain. (In Spanish with English summary).

González, L.M. 1989. *Historia natural del Aguila Imperial Ibérica* Aquila adalberti: *taxonomía, población, análisis de la distribución, alimentación, reproducción y conservación.* Doctoral thesis, Universidad Autónoma de Madrid.

Gottschalk, T. 1995. Zugbeobachtungen am Rotmilan im Hinblick auf Zugverlauf und Zuggeschwindigkeit im Vortaunus/Hessen. In Müller, F. (ed.) *Rotmilan* Milvus milvus, 47-52. Vogel und Umwelt. (In German with English summary).

Gowland, C.H. 1947. The Natural History of the Kite. *Bird Land* 2: 364-367.

Green, B.H. 1979. *Wildlife Introductions to Great Britain.* Report by the Working Group on Introductions of the UK Committee for International Nature Conservation (1979). Nature Conservancy Council, London.

Hagemeijer, W.J.M. & Blair, M.J. (eds.). 1997. *The EBCC Atlas of European Breeding Birds: Their distribution and abundance.* Poyser, London.

Harvie-Brown, J.A. 1906. *A fauna of the Tay Basin and Strathmore.* David Douglas, Edinburgh.

Hazevoet, C.J. 1995. *The Birds of the Cape Verde Islands.* British Ornithologists Union, Tring.

Heredia, B., Alonso, J.C. & Hiraldo, F. 1991. Space and habitat use by Red Kites *Milvus milvus* during winter in the Guadalquivir marshes: a comparison between resident and wintering populations. *Ibis* 133: 374-381.

Heredia, R. 1997. Lammergeier *Gypaetus barbatus* (species account). In Hagemeijer, W.J.M. & Blair, M.J. (eds.) *The EBCC Atlas of European Breeding Birds: Their distribution and abundance.* Poyser, London.

Hernández, M. 1997. *Preliminary report on the illegal poisoning of birds of prey in Spain, September 1995-April 1997.* Laboratorio Forense de Vida Silvestre, Madrid.

Hille, S. 1995a. *Untersuchungen zur Ökologie des Rotmilans* Milvus milvus *in der Rhön.* Masters Thesis, University of Giessen.

Hille, S. 1995b. Nahrungswahl und Jagdstrategien des Rotmilans *Milvus milvus* im Biosphärenreservat Rhön/Hessen. In Müller, F. (ed.) *Rotmilan* Milvus milvus, 99-126. Vogel und Umwelt. (In German with English summary).

Hille, S. 1998. Status of the kites *Milvus milvus fasciicauda* (Hartert, 1914) and *Milvus m. migrans* (Boddaert, 1783) on the Cape Verde Islands. *J. Ornithol.* 139: 73-75. (In German with English summary).

Hiraldo, F., Heredia, B. & Alonso, J.C. 1993. Communal roosting of wintering Red Kites *Milvus milvus*: Social feeding strategies for the exploitation of food resources. *Ethology* 93: 117-124.

Holloway, S. 1996. *The Historical Atlas of Breeding Birds in Britain and Ireland: 1875-1900.* Poyser, London.

Holmes, J., Walker, D., Davies, P. & Carter, I. 2000. *The illegal persecution of raptors in England.* English Nature Research Report No. 343. English Nature, Peterborough.

Hope, C. 1996. Red Kite (species account). In James, P. (ed.). *Birds of Sussex.* Sussex Ornithological Society.

Image, B. 1992. Montagu's Harriers taking prey disturbed by farm machinery. *British Birds* 85: 559.

Janss, G.F.E. 2000. Avian mortality from power lines: a morphologic approach of a species-specific mortality. *Biological Conservation* 95: 353-359.

Jonsson, L. 1992. *Birds of Europe: with North Africa and the Middle East.* Christopher Helm, London.

Jordano, P. 1981. Relaciones interspecificas y coexistencia entre el Águila Real *Aquila Chrysaetos* y el Águila Perdicera *Hieraaetus fasciatus* en Sierra Morena central. *Ardeola* 28: 67-87.

Jørgensen, H.E. 1989. *Danmarks Rovfugle.* Copenhagen.

Kjellén, N. 1996. Project Glada-Årsrapport 1995. [The Red Kite Project 1995] *Anser* 35: 17-25. (In Swedish with English summary).

Kjellén, N. 1999. Project Glada-Årsrapport 1998. [The Red Kite Project 1998] *Anser 38*: 85-89.

Larraz, D.S. 1999. Dumps for dead livestock and the conservation of wintering Red Kites *Milvus milvus. J. Raptor Res.* 33: 338-340.

Lilford, Lord. 1880-1883. *Notes on the Birds of Northamptonshire* Vol. 1. Taylor & Francis, London.

Lockie, J.D., Ratcliffe, D.A. & Balharry, R. 1969. Breeding success and organochlorine residues in Golden Eagles in west Scotland. *J. Appl. Ecol.* 6: 381-389.

Lockwood, P. 1999. Red Kite (species account). In Taylor, M., Seago, M., Allard, P. & Dorling, D. (eds.) *The Birds of Norfolk.* Pica Press, Robertsbridge.

Lovegrove, R. 1990. *The Kite's Tale: The story of the Red Kite in Wales.* RSPB, Sandy.

Lovegrove. R., Elliot, G. & Smith, K. 1990. The Red Kite in Britain. *RSPB Conservation Review* No. 4. RSPB, Sandy.

Mammen, U. & Opitz, H. 2000. *Vogel des Jahres 2000: Der Rotmilan.* NABU, Bonn.

Mammen, U. & Stubbe, M. 1995. Alterseinschätzung und brutbeginn des Rotmilans *Milvus milvus.* In Müller, F. (ed.) *Rotmilan* Milvus milvus, 91-98. Vogel und Umwelt. (In German with English summary).

Marchant, J.H. & Gregory, R.D. 1999. Numbers of nesting Rooks *Corvus frugilegus* in the United Kingdom in 1996. *Bird Study* 46: 258-273.

May, C.A., Wetton, J.H., Davis, P.E., Brookfield, J.F.Y. & Parkin, D.T. 1993. Single-locus profiling reveals loss of variation in inbred populations of the Red Kite *Milvus milvus. Proc. R. Soc. Lond. B* 251: 165-170.

May, C.A., Wetton, J.H. & Parkin, D.T. 1993. Polymorphic sex-specific sequences in birds of prey. *Proc. R. Soc. Lond. B* 253: 271-276.

Mebs, T. 1995. Die besondere Verantwortung der Mitteleuropäer für den rotmilan – status und bestandsentwicklung. In Müller, F. (ed.) *Rotmilan* Milvus milvus, 7-10. Vogel und Umwelt. (In German with English summary).

Medina, M. 2000. *Studies of a breeding pair of Red Kites in central England.* Unpubl. MSc Thesis, Anglia Polytechnic University, Cambridge.

Meretsky, V.J., Snyder, N.F.R., Beissinger, S.R., Clendenen, D.A. & Wiley, J.W. 1999. Demography of the California Condor: Implications for re-establishment. *Conservation Biology* 14: 957-967.

Meyburg, B.-U. & Meyburg, C. 1987. *Present status of diurnal birds of prey in various countries bordering the Mediterranean.* Instituto Nazionale di Biologia della Selvagina XII. Bologne.

Mitchell, F.S. 1892. *The Birds of Lancashire.* Gurney & Jackson, London.

Mock, D.W., Lamey, T.C. & Thomson, D.B.A. 1988. Falsifiability and the Information Center Hypothesis. *Ornis Scand.* 19: 231-248.

Montagu, G. 1833. *Ornithological Dictionary of British Birds.* Orr & Smith, London.

Morrison, S. 1997. *Rare Birds in Dorset.* Privately published, Poole.

Mosimann, P. & Juillard, M. 1988. Brutbestand und winterverbreitung des Rotmilans *Milvus milvus* in der Schweiz. *Orn. Beobachter* 85: 199-206.

Mougeot, F. 2000. Territorial intrusions and copulation patterns in Red Kites *Milvus milvus* in relation to breeding density. *Animal Behaviour* 59: 633-642.

Müller, W. 1995. Brut-und winterbestand des Rotmilans *Milvus milvus* in der Schweiz. In Müller, F. (ed.) *Rotmilan* Milvus milvus, 39-45. Vogel und Umwelt. (In German with English summary).

Muntaner, J. & Mayol, J. (eds.). 1996. *Biology and conservation of Mediterranean raptors, 1994.* SEO Monographía No. 4, Madrid. (In Spanish with English summary).

Newton, I. 1979. *The Population Ecology of Raptors.* Poyser, London.

Newton, I., Davis, P.E. & Davis, J.E. 1989. Age of first breeding, dispersal and survival of Red Kites *Milvus milvus* in Wales. *Ibis* 131: 16-21.

Newton, I., Davis, P.E. & Moss, D. 1981. Distribution and breeding of Red Kites in relation to land-use in Wales. *J. Appl. Ecol.* 18: 173-186.

Newton, I., Davis, P.E. & Moss, D. 1994. Philopatry and population growth of Red Kites *Milvus milvus* in Wales. *Proc. R. Soc. Lond. B* 257: 317-323.

Newton, I., Davis, P.E. & Moss, D. 1996. Distribution and breeding of Red Kites *Milvus milvus* in relation to afforestation and other land-use in Wales. *J. Appl. Ecol.* 33: 210-224.

Newton, I., Shore, R.F., Wyllie, I., Birds, J.D.S. & Dale, L. 1999. Empirical evidence of side-effects of rodenticides on some predatory birds and mammals. In Cowand, D.P. & Feare, C.J. (eds.) *Advances in vertebrate pest management*, 347-367. Filander Verlag, Fürth.

Nicolai, B. 1997. Red Kite *Milvus milvus* (species account). In Hagemeijer, W.J.M. & Blair, M.J. (eds.) *The EBCC Atlas of European Breeding Birds: Their distribution and abundance.* Poyser, London.

Ortlieb, R. 1989. *Der Rotmilan* Milvus milvus. Die Neue Brehm-Bücherei 532, Wittenburg.

Pain, D.J., Amiard-Triquet, C., Bavoux, C., Burneleau, G., Eon, L. & Nicolau-Guillaumet, P. 1993. Lead poisoning in wild populations of Marsh Harriers *Circus aeruginosus* in the Camargue and Charente-Maritime, France. *Ibis* 135: 379-386.

Pain, D.J., Sears, J. & Newton, I. 1995. Lead concentrations in birds of prey in Britain. *Environmental Pollution* 87: 173-180.

Patrimonio, O. 1990. *Le Milan Royal* Milvus milvus *en Corse: répartition et reproduction.* Travaux Scientifiques du Parc Naturel Régional et des Réserves Naturelles de Corse.

Petty, S.J. 1989. Goshawks: Their status, requirements and management. *Forestry Commission Bulletin 81.*

Porstendörfer, D. 1997. Untersuchungen zum aktionsraum des Rotmilans *Milvus milvus* während der Jungenaufzucht. *Vogelkdl. Ber. Niedersachs.* 30: 15-17.

Prakash, V. 1989. Population and distribution of raptors in Keoladeo National Park, Bharatpur, India. In Meyburg, B.-U. & Chancellor, R.D. (eds.) *Raptors in the Modern World,* 129-137. WWGBP, London.

Ratcliffe, D. 1997. *The Raven: A natural history in Britain and Ireland.* Poyser, London.

Reid-Henry, D. & Harrison, C. 1988. *The History of the Birds of Britain.* Collins, London.

Rheinwald, G. 1982. *Brutvogelatlas der Bundesrepublik Deutschland-Kartierung 1980.* Schriftenreihe des Dachverbandes Deutscher Avifaunisten.

Rocamora, G. & Yeatmann-Berthelot, D. 1999. *Oiseaux menacés et à surveiller en France.* SEOF/LPO, Paris.

Rufino, R., Araüjo, A. & Abreu, M. 1985. Breeding raptors in Portugal: distribution and population estimates. In Newton, I. & Chancellor, R.D. (eds.) *Conservation Studies on raptors.* ICBP Technical Publication 5: 3-14. Cambridge.

Sagot, F. 1991. Milan Royal *Milvus milvus.* In Yeatmann-Berthelot, D. & Jarry, G. (eds.) *Atlas des oiseaux de France en hiver,* 146-147. Société Ornithologique de France, Paris.

Sarker, S.U. & Sarker, K. 1985. Birds of prey and their conservation in the Sundarbans Mangrove Forests, Khulna, Bangladesh. In Newton, I. & Chancellor, R.D. (eds.) *Conservation Studies on raptors.* ICBP Technical Publication 5: 205-209. Cambridge.

Schmid, H., Luder, R., Naef-Daenzer, B., Graf, R. & Zbinden, N. 1998. *Atlas des oiseaux nicheurs de Suisse. Distribution des oiseaux nicheurs en Suisse et en Liechtenstein en 1993-1996.* Station Ornithologique Suisse, Sempach.

Sharp, E.A. & Hunter, K. 1999. *The occurrence of second generation anticoagulant rodenticide residues in Red Kites in Scotland.* Scottish Agricultural Science Agency, unpublished report.

Sharrock, J.T.R. & Davies, C. 2000. The European Bird Report: Non-passerines, including near-passerines. *British Birds* 93: 114-128.

Shawyer, C. 1998. *The Barn Owl.* Arlequin Press, Chelmsford.

Shore, R.F., Afsar, A., Horne, J.A. & Wright, J. 2000. *Rodenticide and lead concentrations in Red Kites* Milvus milvus. Centre for Ecology and Hydrology, Huntingdon.

Shore, R.F., Birks, J.D.S., Freestone, P. & Kitchener, A.C. 1996. Second-generation rodenticides and Polecats *Mustela putorius* in Britain. *Environmental Pollution* 91: 279-282.

Snow, D.W. & Perrins, C.M. 1998. *The Birds of the Western Palearctic: Concise Edition* Vol. 1. Oxford University Press, Oxford.

Snyder, N. & Snyder, H. 2000. *The California Condor: A Saga of Natural History and Conservation.* Academic Press, London.

SOVON. 1987. *Atlas van de Nederlandse Vogels.* SOVON, Arnhem (In Dutch with English summary).

Squires, A. & Jeeves, M. 1994. *Leicestershire and Rutland Woodlands: past and present.* Kairos Press, Newton Linford.

Stubbe, M. 1982. Brutdichte und alterstruktur einer Rotmilan-Population *Milvus milvus* – im nördlichen Harzvorland der DDR im vergleich zum Mäusebussard *Buteo buteo. Arch. Naturschutz Landscharftsforschung* 22: 205-214.

Svensson, L., Grant, P.J., Mullarney, K. & Zetterström, D. 1999. *Collins Bird Guide.* HarperCollins, London.

Taylor, K., Hudson, R. & Horne, G. 1988. Buzzard breeding distribution and abundance in Britain and Northern Ireland in 1983. *Bird Study* 35: 109-118.

Thiollay, J.M. & Terrasse, J.F. (eds.). 1984. *Estimation des effectifs de rapaces nicheurs diurnes et non rupestres en France.* Fonds d'Intervention pours les Rapaces, La Garenne-Colombes.

Ticehurst, N.F. 1934. Rewards for vermin-killing paid by the churchwardens of Tenterden 1626-1712. *Hastings and East Sussex Naturalist* 5: 69-82.

Tjernberg, M. 1983. Habitat and nest site features of Golden Eagles *Aquila chrysaetos* in Sweden. *Swedish Wildlife Research* 12: 131-163.

Toms, M.P. & Clark, J.A. 1998. Bird ringing in Britain and Ireland in 1996. *Ringing & Migration* 19: 95-167.

Tubbs, C.R. 1974. *The Buzzard.* Newton Abbot.

Tucker, G.M. & Heath, M.F. (eds.). 1994. *Birds in Europe: Their Conservation Status.* Birdlife International, Cambridge.

Urcun, J-P. & Bried, J. 1998. The autumn migration of Red Kite *Milvus milvus* through the Pyrenees. In Chancellor, R.D., Meyburg, B.-U. & Ferrero, J.J. (eds.) *Holarctic Birds of Prey: Proceedings of an International Conference,* 641-654. ADENEX/WWGBP, Calamonte, Spain.

Van den Berg, A.B. & Bosman, C.A.W. 1999. *Rare Birds of the Netherlands.* Pica Press, Mountfield.

Van Kleef, H. & Bustamante, J. 1999. First recorded polygynous mating in the Red Kite *Milvus milvus. J. Raptor Res.* 33: 254-257.

Veiga, J.P. & Hiraldo, F. 1990. Food habits and the survival and growth of nestlings in two sympatric kites (*Milvus milvus* and *Milvus migrans*). *Holarct. Ecol.* 13: 62-71.

Villafuerte, R., Viñuela, J. & Blanco, J.C. 1998. Extensive predator persecution caused by population crash in a game species: The case of Red Kites and Rabbits in Spain. *Biological Conservation* 84: 181-188.

Village, A. 1990. *The Kestrel.* Poyser, London.

Viñuela, J. 1992, 1993, 1994. *Status of the Red Kite in Spain – Red Kite Project Research Reports.* SEO/Birdlife, Madrid.

Viñuela, J. 1996. Situacion del Milano Real *Milvus milvus* en el Mediterraneo. In Muntaner, J. & Mayol, J. (eds.) *Biology and conservation of Mediterranean raptors, 1994,* 90-100. SEO Monographía No. 4, Madrid. (In Spanish with English summary).

Viñuela, J. 1997. Road transects as a large-scale census method for raptors: the case of the Red Kite *Milvus milvus* in Spain. *Bird Study* 44: 155-165.

Viñuela, J. & Ferrer, M. 1997. Regulation of growth in Red Kites and Imperial Eagles. *Wilson Bull.* 109: 92-101.

Viñuela, J., Martí, R. & Ruiz, A. 1999. *El Milano Real en España.* SEO/Birdlife Monografía No. 6, Madrid.

Walters Davies, P. & Davis, P.E. 1973. The ecology and conservation of the Red Kite in Wales. *British Birds* 66: 183-224, 241-269.

Ward, P. & Zahavi, A. 1973. The importance of certain assemblages of birds as 'information centres' for finding food. *Ibis* 115: 517-534.

Warren, R.B. 1989. Red Kite and Black Kite following mowing-machine. *British Birds* 82: 116.

Watson, J. 1997. *The Golden Eagle.* Poyser. London.

Weber, M. & Stubbe, M. 1995. Biometrische Untersuchungen zu Eischalenveränderungen bei Rotmilan *Milvus milvus*, Schwarzmilan *Milvus migrans* und Mäusebussard *Buteo buteo* nach 1950. In Müller, F. (ed.) *Rotmilan Milvus milvus*, 133-139. Vogel und Umwelt. (In German with English summary).

Wiebe, K.L., Korpimäki, E. & Wiehn, J. 1998. Hatching asynchrony in Eurasian Kestrels in relation to the abundance and predictability of cyclic prey. *J. An. Ecol* 67: 908-917,

Wildman, L., O'Toole, L. & Summers, R.W. 1998. The diet and foraging behaviour of the Red Kite in Scotland. *Scottish Birds* 19: 134-140.

Yarrell, W. 1857. *History of British Birds* (revised edition). Van Voorst, London.

INDEX